THE WORLD'S GREAT LAKES

Books by Ferdinand C. Lane

THE WORLD'S GREAT LAKES

THE MYSTERIOUS SEA

FERDINAND C. LANE

The World's
Great Lakes

DOUBLEDAY & COMPANY, INC.

Garden City, New York

1948

THE AGE OF LAKES

The earth is now passing through that period of its troubled history which geologists know as the lacustrine era, or the Age of Lakes. As the continental icecaps that covered so much of our northern landscape melted, their surplus waters collected in tens of thousands of Nature's reservoirs. Many of these have already disappeared; many more are rapidly evaporating; the world is drying up.

Great areas formerly well watered and fertile are desert now. Northern Africa, once the granary of Rome, has been swallowed up by the ever expanding Sahara; in southern Africa the Kalahari and other deserts are encroaching upon lush grasslands and tropical forests; Australia is a hollow shell surrounding a vast region of sun-parched emptiness. The painted deserts of Utah and Nevada were carved by swollen torrents. Central Asia is blighted by a growing desiccation, a veritable wasting sickness. There lakes by the thousands have vanished, and once great rivers are absorbed by shifting sands which have also buried many a ruined city. Against this global malady it is high time that we enlisted those stout allies—Our Friendly Lakes.

GREAT LAKE DEPTHS AND AREAS

Statistics on the great lakes of the world are necessarily incomplete. This is particularly true of maximum depths, for surface levels change and bottom contours are seldom fully charted. Lake areas are variously given in standard atlases and encyclopedias not only because of fragmentary data but also because of the transient nature of lakes themselves. These cannot be plotted like farm lands or city lots. Shore lines are indefinite in dying lakes like Chad or Bangweulu, and unstable in fluctuating lakes like Great Salt Lake or Urmia in Persia. Improved surveys are being conducted in Canada and the Russian dominions, but much work remains to be done. Hence the figures incorporated in this volume lay no claim to absolute accuracy, but they have been carefully revised in the light of all available records.

A LIST OF THE WORLD'S BIG LAKES IN THE COMPARATIVE ORDER OF THEIR SIZE

This tabulation presents the most recent and reliable data. However, some lake borders are extremely variable, some have never been surveyed, and a few figures are mere estimates.

	Lake	Sq. Miles	Continent
1.	Caspian Sea	169,300	Asia–Europe
2.	Superior	31,820	North America
3.	Aral Sea	26,233	Asia
4.	Victoria Nyanza	26,200	Africa
5.	Huron	23,010	North America
6.	Michigan	22,400	North America
7.	Baikal	13,300	Asia
8.	Tanganyika	12,700	Africa
9.	Great Bear Lake	11,490	North America
10.	Great Slave Lake	11,170	North America
11.	Nyasa	11,000	Africa
12.	Erie	9,940	North America
13.	Winnipeg	9,390	North America
14.	Ontario	7,540	North America
15.	Balkhash	7,115	Asia
16.	Ladoga	7,000	Europe
17.	Chad	6,500[1]	Africa
18.	Maracaibo	4,000[2]	South America
19.	Onega	3,764	Europe
20.	Eyre	3,700[3]	Australia
21.	Rudolf	3,475	Africa
22.	Titicaca	3,200	South America
23.	Nicaragua	3,089	North America
24.	Athabaska	3,085	North America
25.	Reindeer	2,444	North America
26.	Issyk-Kul	2,230	Asia

27.	Torrens	2,230[3]	Australia
28.	Vener	2,149	Europe
29.	Nettilling	2,100	North America
30.	Winnipegosis	2,086	North America
31.	Van	2,000	Asia
32.	Hamun (Seistan)	2,000[4]	Asia
33.	Tung Ting	2,000[5]	Asia
34.	Bangweulu	1,900	Africa
35.	Urmia	1,750[6]	Asia
36.	Great Salt Lake	1,750[6]	North America
37.	Manitoba	1,711	North America
38.	Dubawnt	1,654	North America
39.	Albert Nyanza	1,640	Africa
40.	Gairdner	1,600[3]	Australia
41.	Nipigon	1,590	North America
42.	Lake of the Woods	1,485	North America

Several others might perhaps be included, such as Kivu and the Makarikari Playa in Africa, Tonlè-sap in Cambodia, Koko Nor in greater China, and particularly Lagôa dos Patos, which fills a drowned valley near the seacoast of Rio Grande do Sul in Brazil and is reported to be 124 miles long with a maximum width of 37 miles.

[1]Outline too indefinite for more than a rough estimate.
[2]Maracaibo sometimes considered a lagoon rather than a lake.
[3]A playa or periodic lake.
[4]According to Tate's map.
[5]Maximum.
[6]Mean area between wide variations.

Contents

xii   *Contents*

IV
AFRICAN LAKES

V

ASIAN LAKES

VI
AUSTRALIAN LAKES

VII
EUROPEAN LAKES

VIII
NORTH AMERICAN LAKES

IX

SOUTH AMERICAN LAKES

X

LAKES AND CIVILIZATION

XI
MAN INTRUDES UPON THE STAGE

XI
MAN INTRUDES UPON THE STAGE

I

Introduction

FOREWORD

Lakes! What a fascinating chapter in the story of our planet
may be read from their origin, their growth and development,
their decline and tragic disappearance. And how varied they
are. Could we find sharper contrasts than the tropic gem the
Martin Johnsons discovered in Africa, to christen Lake Paradise, and—shall we say—the unwholesome, almost poisonous
surface of the Dead Sea?

For lakes are not mere puddles of surplus rain water, but
impressive features of the landscape woven into the global
pattern. With few exceptions, they are transient features, too,
less enduring than mountains or rivers; their life span, long as
it may seem, but a brief hour in the hoary age of continents
and seas. A few, a very few, may have mirrored the passing
clouds for millions of years, but almost all are more recent
phenomena. Some have just been born; the vast majority are
slowly dying; many thousands are already dead.

Lakes, like dramatic characters, have personalities all their
own. Some are subtly alluring; others merely pleasing; others,
saline or alkaline, may appear repulsive, like crusted scabs
upon the face of nature; while a few are even a bit terrifying.

So at least thought Sir Alfred Sharpe, the English explorer,
on his expedition of 1912–13 to Kivu, the "most beautiful lake
in Africa." While yet two days' march distant, he heard
rumblings like muffled artillery, and the sky at night reflected

an angry glare. Arrived upon the southern shore, he gazed across sixty miles of water at dense clouds of smoke billowing up across the jungle. Hiring a native boat, he crossed the lake to become involved in an awe-inspiring program of creation tense with danger. From a volcanic cone, newly risen from beds of ancient scoria, two molten rivers flowed into an inlet of the lake that boiled like a cauldron as clouds of steam rose hundreds of feet. Countless dead fish floated upon the surface, which was agitated as from hidden whirlpools. Meanwhile a fresh outburst of red-hot rock and sizzling mud drove the adventurers, against their will, right through those seething waters to a precarious refuge on the shore. The heat was unbearable, the noise deafening—it was heard on the shores of Victoria Nyanza, a hundred and ninety miles away! But just such eruptions, by damming up rivers, had created Kivu, beautiful but terrific, in the heart of Africa.

Poles apart in content and appearance, and half a world away, lies that vast Canadian sea of fresh waters called Great Slave Lake. Its wooded shores and rocky islands, the haunt of innumerable wild fowl, and its thickets, rustling to shy red deer or crackling to the tread of lumbering moose, led a simple-minded native to ask Warburton Pike if "heaven were more beautiful than the country of the musk ox in summer, when sometimes the mist blows over the lakes and sometimes the water is blue, and the loons cry very often."

The inherent charm or bizarre setting of many a lake is heightened by historic association. No wonder nomad horsemen, gazing upon Baikal with superstitious awe, called it Dalai Nor—the Holy Lake; or that Zor-Kol in the lofty Pamirs, "the world's white rooftree," visited long ago by such renowned travelers as Hsüan Tsang and Marco Polo, was known to the Chinese as the Dragon Pool; or that Peruvian natives regard those cyclopean ruins around Lake Titicaca, the cradle of the Inca race, as the work of supernatural beings.

And we, who smile at such primitive fancies, surely revere that sunken bowl of waters called the Sea of Galilee.

Really, we should know more about these courageous allies of ours, the lakes, in their battle against hostile elements. For whether natural reservoirs of fresh water or mines of mineral, they temper summer heat and winter cold, moisten our atmosphere, and delay a menacing aridity. They beautify our landscape, yield inspiration to artists and poets, and are a source of spiritual exaltation and calm. And what has Man, the ignorant, the indifferent, the blunderer, done but misuse their bounties and hasten their inevitable decline? Surely, they deserve more appreciation—our friendly lakes!

DEFINITION AND CLASSIFICATION

Before discussing a subject so vague and complex, we had best define our terms. Just what is a lake, anyway? The common notion, "a body of water surrounded by land," will hardly do, for that would describe the Black Sea, or even the Mediterranean. Neither can we limit the term to "fresh water," for some lakes are saltier than the ocean; nor bar them from contact with the latter, for most lakes have outlets.

The name "lake" comes from the Latin *lacus*, also meaning basin or tank. That study of the subject called limnology is perhaps the youngest of the sciences, for it is little more than half a century old. The father of limnology, Professor François Alphonse Forel, of Switzerland, defined a lake as a mass of still water situated in a depression of the ground without direct communication with the sea.

Webster adds further light: "A lake is a considerable inland body of standing water; also, an expanded part of a river." This seems clear until we study the adjective "considerable."

Just what does that mean? In America a small lake is usually
a pond, but the distinction is indefinite. While many lakes are
less than a mile across, I once camped in Alberta on the shores
of a splendid oval body of water eighteen miles long called
Gull Pond. Besides, by a favorite device of summer-resort
literature, a prosaic Duck Pond is transformed into a more
aristocratic Swan Lake.

Delving further into Mr. Webster's fine print, we discover
that depth, no less than size, is a consideration; for he informs
us that a lake so shallow that aquatic plants grow in most of it
is a pond, while a "pond that has become largely choked with
vegetation, is a marsh."

Elsewhere in the world lake names are more phonetically
appropriate. The natives in Central Africa called their vast
inland seas nyanzas, a majestic title for Victoria Nyanza, the
second most extensive body of fresh water in the world. There
is also a barbaric ring in the Mongol Nor of Tengri Nor, and
the Kirghiz Kul in Issyk-Kul, those queer lakes of Central
Asia. The Irish loughs and the Scottish lochs are distinctive,
as are the English meres and waters in such landscape favorites
as Windermere or Durwentwater. The English also favor calling diminutive lakes tarns or pools, more colorful than simple
"ponds."

A few lakes are termed "great," though with the same lack
of discrimination that bestowed the title upon Tsar Peter and
Catherine of Muscovy and denied it to Elizabeth of England
and Napoleon. Thus we have Great Salt Lake in Utah and
Great Slave Lake in Canada, impressive bodies of water, but
minor compared with Superior or even Huron.

We might suppose that "sea" would connote imposing
dimensions, and so it does in the Caspian or Aral; but how
about the Sea of Galilee?

Many lakes deserve recognition apart from size. Nettilling,
in desolate Baffin Land, is seventy miles long, yet few white

men have ever seen it, while even wandering Eskimos visit it
rarely. How unimportant it seems compared with tiny Walden
Pond, where Thoreau withdrew from the world to meditate
upon the follies of society, although Nettilling could engulf
a thousand Walden Ponds. Yet if we should attempt to grade
lakes by their influence upon human affairs, we should cause
confusion worse confounded.

Other classifications have been proposed, such as the composition of the water, which would separate fresh-water lakes
from salt, like scriptural sheep from the goats.

Lakes could also be differentiated by their altitudes, ranging
from the Dead Sea's 1292 feet below the level of the ocean to
Titicaca's 12,507 feet above, or the still loftier lakes of Tibet
and the Himalayas. Depth, too, might be considered, varying
from Baikal's 5413-foot abysses to the 15-foot shallows of
Bangweulu and Winnipegosis or the mere watery films of the
so-called Soda Lakes.

Color would hardly do, for lake waters range through all
possible shades from almost white to nearly black, while the
bottom is often revealed through transparent shallows or the
images of sky or cloud or forest reflected from the surface.

Size, in spite of its deficiencies, is the best gauge for culling
the world's important lakes from the lesser fry, for it is the one
recognized characteristic in the features of topography, be
they mountain, desert, river, or lake.

Even here we must accept some arbitrary standard, or we
shall have too many specimens for this restricted study. Hence
we shall limit our survey mainly to those lakes with an area of
1500 or more square miles. At that there are over forty such,
a greater number than we expected to find when we began our
search for them.

They seem to fall into definite categories. First is the Caspian, that super lake, so vast that it is seldom regarded as a
lake at all, although it fulfills every detail of Webster's defini-

tion. Next in order are five great lakes, led by Superior, which are in a class by themselves, as they exceed 20,000 square miles. Below them is a third group ranging from 13,000 square miles or better down to 7000, some ten or more. Still further down the ladder are seven decreasing from 7000 to 3000; while a more numerous group of nearly twenty trail away to our lower limit of 1500 square miles. In some cases where surveys are still incomplete, distinctions cannot be too clearly drawn.

First, however, we must glance at the nature and history of lakes, their origin and ceaseless struggle for existence in a changing world.

GLOBAL DISTRIBUTION

Any large-scale map will show that lakes are most unevenly distributed. Antarctica was supposed to have none at all until Captain Charles A. Bond, one of the fliers with the Byrd Expedition, reported a singular region some forty miles in width where, amid dark brown, conical hills, nestled several lakes "of a pale green, muddy color, interspersed with dark blue and light green." Aside from mountainous regions, lakes are also scarce throughout much of western Europe, India, and South America. In the latter continent this is particularly noteworthy, for lakes are often an integral part of river systems, and South America is unrivaled in its rivers.

To offset such sterile territory, other regions seem pitted, as though by smallpox, with lakes of every conceivable size and shape. From a limited section of Michigan more than five thousand are reported; Minnesota has over ten thousand lakes; Florida, over thirty thousand, while Finland, still more generously supplied, numbers its lakes well above sixty thousand. In Canada, however, they seem to riot in the greatest profusion, for throughout those vast forested regions and the barren lands which stretch northward to the Arctic they spatter the landscape in numbers that seem literally beyond all counting.

The Western Hemisphere has been blessed with much better than its share of global fresh waters. Where South American rivers predominate, led by the peerless Amazon, North America is the continent of lakes. Three of the six super lakes (those over 20,000 square miles) are located there, while the same proportion seems to continue through other categories. Hence we are justified in assuming that half of all the lakes on earth are in North America.

This concentration is even more pronounced, for, excepting Lake Michigan, Great Salt Lake, and Nicaragua, all the other largest North American lakes, and a decided majority of the smaller ones, are partly or wholly Canadian. Nature has dealt harshly with that country in a rigorous climate, a desolate Arctic archipelago, and great areas of rocky or tundra-covered mainland almost as sparsely settled as when they comprised the hunting grounds of nomad Indians or Eskimos. But she has fairly deluged the landscape with lakes.

In contrast with such prodigality, South America is poorly endowed. Aside from mountainous areas with Titicaca, and such lagoons as the Caribbean Maracaibo, there are no important lakes and, except where rivers overflow, few lakes of any kind. In Europe, apart from Alpine regions, lakes are mainly collected in the north, where three at least—Ladoga and Onega in Russia and Vener in Sweden—qualify for our list.

Asia is so vast that we would expect a wide variety in her topography. With Europe she shares the hugest of lakes, the Caspian, and also includes the Aral Sea within her boundaries. In the Near East, Van, emprisoned among Armenian mountains, merits attention; Persia has Lake Urmia and the weird Seistan region bordering Afghanistan, while the central continent presents elongated Balkhash, Issyk-Kul of fabulous history, and above all, Baikal, in many respects the most interesting of lakes.

Africa, however, bears the closest resemblance to North America, for in the heart of that continent, surrounded by still smoldering volcanoes, lies the only cluster that can challenge our Great Lakes. There are five of these African giants— Victoria, in area Superior's closest rival; Tanganyika, longest of fresh-water lakes; deep and beautiful Nyasa; Rudolf, bitterly alkaline; Albert Nyanza; and several lesser but still imposing associates. Africa also has its dying Chad, half smothered by the sands of the Sahara, Bangweulu, choked with papyrus and elephant grass, and the great Makarikari Basin in Bechuanaland.

Quite as interesting as the latter is that group of shallow lakes that once covered the sunken south-central portion of Australia. Enormous in their original extent, the outlines of three at least—Eyre and Torrens and Gairdner—are expansive enough for inclusion in our list. But whether they are lakes in the final stages of dissolution, or lakes already dead, whose dry bones bleach in the blazing sun together with those of giant extinct wombats and wallabies, is a problem that must await a later excursion into that never-never land.

How many lakes lie scattered over the world no one knows. Even estimates are hazardous. Professor Welch, an authority on the subject, thinks they total several hundred thousand. In North America alone he estimates their combined area at 225,000 square miles, which seems conservative in view of Canada's legions of unnamed and unsurveyed bodies of fresh water. It would be far better for our global climate and fertility of soil if these natural humidors and reserves of moisture were more equitably distributed.

II

How Lakes Are Formed

In the development of lakes, like the serving of soup, two things are necessary—the bowl and its contents. Nor are the two invariably found together, for empty crockery on the shelf is matched in nature by such appalling gulfs as Death Valley, far below sea level yet oppressed by one of the driest atmospheres on earth. In vivid contrast are regions like upper Canada, where even the tiniest bowl seems to be overflowing and the vast continental table, to employ a homely figure of speech, is sopping wet.

In a study of lakes structural factors predominate; hence the bowl should be examined first. Lake beds are formed in several ways. First, they occur as natural depressions; second, they are gouged out or built up by the forces of erosion; third, they are produced by a rending apart of surface strata; and, fourth, they result from those gigantic paroxysms known as volcanic action. These four comprise the vast architectural blueprints for resculpturing the global surface, the groundwork in lake formation. Other methods, though sometimes spectacular, are relatively unimportant.

NATURAL DEPRESSIONS

Simplest of all lake origins is the accumulation of surplus rain in natural depressions among hills or rolling uplands, for continental surfaces are never level. These depressions may vary in size from basins no larger than artificial goldfish pools to such enormous areas as embrace Victoria Nyanza, the second largest of fresh-water lakes.

Similar depressions are formed by the warping of the rock strata in a continuous readjustment of global contours. The intervals between rock folds may be amazingly deep—a mile or more in that gigantic trough occupied by Lake Baikal.

Extreme folding is most evident in mountain regions where numerous pockets appear, frequently deep, though usually of no great extent. These become permanent reservoirs, for mountain ranges are titanic combs carding the clouds, like wool, for their moisture, which descends in showers or is stored at freezing altitudes in a never failing reserve of melting snows. Lake Geneva fills such a pocket.

Continental distortions shut off great areas from the sea, forming interior drainage basins like those of Central Asia. Rivers, forced inland, seek the lowest levels to accumulate in lakes where none would otherwise appear. Balkhash and Issyk-Kul are examples. A variant of such basins develops where rising land masses enprison a plateau among still higher ranges. Lake Titicaca, loftiest of big lakes, has been thrust bodily skyward by the upsurging of the Andes. Lakes also dot the more ponderous tableland of Tibet.

Less notable disturbances provide basins ready made by recapturing portions of the sea. This process may be observed on certain coasts, where salt-water inlets or lagoons are sealed off by barrier beaches heaped up by wave action or by drifting sand dunes. Lake Alexandrina in Australia, at the mouth of the great Murray River, is a good illustration.

Uptilting rock strata upon a grander scale have accounted for such lakes as Ladoga, divorced from the Baltic to become the largest fresh-water lake in Europe. Still more imposing is the Caspian, separated long ago from a greater Mediterranean.

Water seeks a common level, as every housewife realizes

when she mops the kitchen floor. And the same force which moistens inequalities in her linoleum is manifested upon a grander scale in many a well-known lake.

EROSION BASINS

Natural depressions, however they came about, are usually modified by the great agents of erosion. Sometimes they are etched more deeply, sometimes built up by dams of detritus, sometimes smoothed away entirely as nature's designs are engraved upon the landscape only to be erased and engraved anew.

In this drama of perpetual change water plays the leading role. Rains wash away the soil and eat into the solid rock. Rivers using such abrasive material grind out deeper, broader valleys. Then some intrusion of lava from the heated interior, or a more fundamental uptilting of rock strata, transforms a valley into an enclosed basin and a lake is born.

Geologists believe that our own Great Lakes occupy what was originally an extensive natural depression. Here rivers that have long since disappeared wore down broad valleys, not unlike that of the Ohio, to excavate such basins as those of Superior and Huron.

Water in the form of ice has added potency, although its operations are limited. Glaciers have made a lake bed of many an Alpine gorge. But the work of such frozen rivers was magnified a thousandfold by those enormous ice fields which once overspread so much of North America, Eurasia, and lesser regions.

On this continent ice radiated from three widely separated focuses until 4,000,000 square miles groaned beneath the burden of a congealed ocean. This restless inundation, which may have reached a thickness of 10,000 feet, used boulders weighing thousands of tons as edged tools. No wonder the soil was peeled away from the Canadian barrens and the exposed rock bruised and abraded everywhere. It is believed that the basins of the Great Lakes were excavated still more deeply in this manner.

The concentration of such enormous volumes of water in ice fields lowered ocean levels and expanded seacoasts all over the world. Then much of Finland settled beneath the crushing weight of ice, the North Sea was all but emptied, while the Baltic slowly changed from a gigantic refrigerator to a huge fresh-water lake. Countless gougings of the earth surface became convenient catch basins for the melting ice which sullenly retreated, while the men of the Stone Age emerged from their drafty caverns and the hairy mammoth and the woolly rhinoceros ranged farther northward. Such territory is richer in lakes than all the rest of the world, for glacial action has been the chief agent in lake formation.

Water in the form of steam becomes a Titan of terrifying potentialities. But though its appearance in geysers and volcanic outbursts is spectacular, steam has been a minor factor in lake structure.

Far more important are those inevitable products of erosion, lateral or terminal moraines. Water in its various forms not only wears down but builds up. Matter scraped from the rocks is not all dumped into the sea. Much of it is merely redistributed on the face of the land. Here rivers play a part, as does the sea in coastal areas, but ice action is predominant. Many a mountain lake was dammed up by a glacial moraine, while the continental ice fields performed a major operation in plastic surgery on the face of the earth. The shore lines and outlets of our Great Lakes, as well as a host of lesser ones, may often be traced in moraines.

Even standing water is an erosive agent, for it is that universal solvent which the alchemists of the Middle Ages sought among their weird paraphernalia of crucibles and cabalistic symbols. Some lakes which dot the Florida landscape were thus eaten out of the coral rock. Subterranean lakes in limestone regions have a similar origin. Sometimes when wall supports give way, the roof caves in to form such pools as those in Yucatán, which were so venerated by the ancient Mayans that they became the scene of human sacrifice.

Nor is water the only agent of erosion. Winds are worthy allies. The uncanny Seistan region of eastern Persia has been deepened, if not in fact formed, by wind action, as have several curious depressions in northern Africa. Like water, also, the winds are quite impartial, creating and destroying with equal indifference. Many a shallow lake is filling up with windblown particles. Chad, one of the most intriguing of big lakes, seems to be slowly suffocating in the sandstorms of the Sahara.

And so every falling drop of water and every passing breeze may aid in creating a new lake or obliterating an old one.

TECTONIC LAKES

A third type of lakes owe their origin to shattered rock strata. Cracks in the earth crust produce deep fissures, in which lakes may collect, or block out areas which subside to form catch basins. Lakes which result from such rending of the global crust are called tectonic.

On February 7, 1812, Eliza Bryan, of New Madrid, in western Tennessee heard what she described as "an awful noise," followed by various alarming phenomena. From fissures in the ground sand and water erupted as the air grew heavy with nauseous sulphur fumes. Such disturbances were the culmination of a series of earth tremors and rumblings which had occasioned uneasiness in that sparsely settled neighborhood ever since the previous autumn.

When these diabolical manifestations—for they were plainly from the Devil—came to an end, the level of New Madrid had subsided twelve feet or more. Still more arresting was the appearance of a new lake, a curious body of water about 14 miles long by 4 in breadth, the overflow of the neighboring Mississippi into a shallow depression where the earth crust had given way.

Reelfoot Lake, as it is now called, is a wild-life sanctuary where numerous bird species, including the bald eagle, are free from molestation. Cypress trees shadow its inky waters, which are infested with enormous catfish. It is a dismal region beloved by writers of the gruesome or unearthly. For the geologist it holds a special interest as a lake that was born almost literally in a night; for the layman, it is instructive as an example of what has occurred elsewhere in the formation of some of the world's most voluminous lakes.

Tectonic action is most noticeable in that colossal earth crack known as the African Rift, which slices through eastern Asia and far down the Dark Continent for at least one sixth the circumference of the globe. Among the well-known lakes that fill its deeper recesses are the Dead Sea, Albert Nyanza, Nyasa, and, hugest of all, Tanganyika. Above the latter's shore line the edges of the Rift tower in sheer cliffs 3000 feet high, while in its deepest abysses the sounding line has run out nearly a mile.

Other lakes have been caused by a blocking out and falling in of enormous areas. This is particularly evident in southern Australia, where the beds of former big lakes lie in a region of depression that has subsided considerably below sea level.

Tectonic lakes, though much less numerous than natural depressions or those ground out by the agents of erosion, are of special interest as evidences of more abrupt and violent disturbance.

VOLCANIC ACTION

At various times in the troubled history of our planet great lava floods have gushed forth. Not infrequently these have formed lakes, either by damming rivers or creating extensive depressions. The process is still in operation in Africa, where the Mfumbiro volcanoes, uprearing from the floor of the Great Rift, have obstructed northern outlets to form one of the strangest of lakes—Kivu.

Isolated volcanoes are also prolific breeders of crater lakes, for the core of an extinct cone is a natural bowl. Most famous of the type is Crater Lake, a favorite beauty spot in Oregon. Lying at an elevation of 6164 feet above sea level, it fills the dead heart of Mount Mazama, whose smoking crest once rose several thousand feet higher still. The wreckage of this great pile survives in surrounding cliffs a thousand feet high. The waters, 6¼ miles long by 4½ wide, are vividly blue, and register an extreme depth of 1996 feet. Wizard Island, rising from the submerged floor, is itself a perfect crater, while another wonder islet is known from its jagged outline as the Phantom Ship.

A similar lake is forming in the Alaskan peninsula in the crater of burnt-out Aniakchak. Here the depression, even more extensive than Crater Lake, is only partially filled, as the accumulating waters have forced an outlet through a break in the rim.

Oregon's Crater Lake is pure, but many others are heavily charged with mineral which affects the color. Of three closely associated lakes in the island of Timor in the East Indies, one is sapphire-blue, another opaque turquoise, the third garnet-red.

In the famous Taupo volcanic zone, which traverses the North Island of New Zealand, lie a number of small but decidedly queer lakes. The region is a fracture of the earth crust, 160 miles long, with a maximum width of about 25. Volcanic energy is everywhere evident, particularly in hot springs and geysers. About the year 1900 the Waimangu Geyser burst forth with unparalleled violence. Steaming water, sand, and even small boulders with a combined weight estimated at 800 tons shot upward to a reported height of 1500 feet. This appalling cataclysm continued about once daily until, 1904, when it subsided for fifty-four days, only to resume activity upon a reduced scale. Later a lake about 130 feet long by 80 wide and very deep appeared in the throat of the geyser, which may be gathering energy for a new outburst. From this seething pool a stream of hot water flows into Rotomahana, a crater lake some three miles long, where it remains separated from the surrounding cold water.

The Taupo Valley has witnessed other startling occurrences. In 1917 a region of hot springs known as Frying Pan Flats blew up, to be replaced by a steaming lake. Another lake in neighboring Inferno Crater remains tranquil for fifteen days, sinking forty feet below the crater rim, then, gathering impetus, its acid waters overflow for four days, only to subside once more. Meanwhile, in the crater of Ruapehu, the loftiest mountain on North Island, 9175 feet high, a lake of hot water is surrounded by glistening snowdrifts.

Dangerous in process of formation, crater lakes may remain so. Exploring the island of San Domingo, Mr. F. S. Fadelle found at an elevation of 2425 feet a curious lake surrounded by the usual vertical cliffs. This lake, though only about 200 feet long by half as broad, was so deep that a 200-foot sounding line failed to touch bottom. Mr. Fadelle noted fumes of sulphureted hydrogen (hydrogen sulphide). A previous visitor probably noted them also, but did not report them, for both he and his native guide were overcome and perished on the shores of this sinister body of water. Even 7 parts of sulphureted hydrogen to 10,000 parts of air may prove fatal.

This lake overflows intermittently into a neighboring stream known as Pointe Mulatte. The waters, usually calm, may boil furiously for days on end. No geyser action is apparent, but that ominous agitation indicates some connection with the heated interior.

Like crater lakes, isolated geysers and hot-spring areas are widely scattered over the earth. The famous thermal fields in Iceland, and the Yellowstone National Park, are too well known to need more than mention here.

Lakes of similar origin sometimes well up from the interior without the usual frightening manifestations. In 1920 Captain J. E. Phillips reported a singular occurrence in the Uganda region of Africa, where volcanic energy is still manifest upon a gigantic scale. In a deep valley where no lake or even stream had ever been known, a lake 300 feet long and 14 feet deep welled up in a single night. Thirty-two hapless natives who had gone to sleep never awakened—not drowned, but overcome by poisonous fumes.

Earth's hidden fires, though banked by rock and soil, are always smoldering, ready to burst forth through vent or fracture or by violent rending asunder of rock strata. Although lakes formed by such outbursts of internal energy are far less numerous or extensive than those of glacial origin, they are more impressive.

EXPLOSIVE CALDERA

In Ashanti, on the African Gold Coast, lies a lake so mysterious that it deserves mention in spite of its diminutive size. The

natives call it Bosumptwe, look upon it as supernatural, and
surround it with deferential taboos.

Roughly circular and about five miles in diameter, Bosumptwe lies in a depression whose slopes are smothered in verdure.
These form precipitous escarpments varying in height from
900 to 1200 feet. From the outside they are less steep and
forbidding, though they appear as a singular ring of hills from
300 to 600 feet high.

There is no evidence that any river ever flowed through
Bosumptwe; while the nearest lake is in Nigeria, some five
hundred miles away. There is no outlet, but water levels are
sustained by streamlets descending that curious escarpment
fed by an annual rainfall of some 65 inches.

A crater lake, one might suppose, but this region has never
known a volcano. How then explain Bosumptwe? Was there a
sinking of the earth crust, like the Great African Rift? Did a
lake form because the bottom fell in? No, rifts are not circular,
nor is there evidence of such action here.

Malcolm Maclarer, the first European to investigate
Bosumptwe, was struck by the similarity to another strange
depression halfway round the world. In Arizona, near the
Canyon Diablo, a cavernous pit 4200 feet in diameter and 440
feet deep marks the spot where a colossal meteorite with a
minimum weight estimated at 1,000,000 tons came hurtling in
from outer space at a speed that may have approached fifty
miles per second. The appalling heat generated by that impact
pulverized the solid rock and caused the contents of the crater
to boil outward, an eruption that in a single instant displaced
some 200,000,000 tons, "equal," according to William Bout-
well, "to a quarter of the amount of material removed in
excavating the Panama Canal."

This impact raised a rim 130 feet high all about the edge of
the pit, and showered fragments of meteoric iron over an area
nine miles in diameter. Sandstone strata deep within the earth

were ground literally to powder, and rock splinters hurled outward in every direction, one such of an estimated weight of 7000 tons!

And so, reasoned Maclarer, was not Bosumptwe the grave of a huger meteorite? True, no iron fragments had been discovered in its vicinity, but most meteorites are stone, and stone would have disintegrated in the terrific pressure and heat of the impact.

Later geologists, however, have challenged Bosumptwe's meteoric origin. Its enormous size in contrast with Diablo has aroused skepticism, while another symptom of earth's internal activities offers a readier explanation. This is the caldera theory, which resembles, yet is unlike, volcanic action. According to this theory, a mass of molten magma, rising where overlying strata were relatively thin, set off a violent explosion of gases combined with superheated steam that literally blew out a hole through the earth crust. Then, as the magma cooled and subsided, the bottom of this hole fell in. Such an upheaval would account for Bosumptwe with less strain upon the imagination, for caldera are found elsewhere, some even larger than this lake's enormous rim.

Unlike volcanoes, which are phenomena of mountainous regions, or have become mountains themselves, caldera may appear in level areas and mark a single violent explosion. But whatever its origin, Bosumptwe is mysterious enough to excuse African natives, who gaze awe-struck upon its sometimes strangely agitated waters.

LAKES OF METEORIC ORIGIN

A few strange lakes are definitely of meteoric origin.

Not only are the lower levels of the famous Diablo crater in

Arizona clogged with quicksand, but there are other evidences of water. The gigantic pit was formerly a lake.

Just when the flaming projectile struck has been fixed within historic time, for the growth of cedars inside the rim and the weathering of rock fragments suggest a date between seven hundred and five thousand years ago.

Besides, there are similar lakes whose origin is incontestable. One group is found in the Gran Chaco of northern Argentina, near the railway station of Gancedo, the largest some 250 by 200 feet. Known since the days of the Spanish Conquest in 1576 as the Campo del Cielo craters, they were supposed to be volcanic, although the nearest Andean mountain of fire and smoke is over five hundred miles away. Recent investigations, however, place them in that strangest of all categories, meteoric. Many metallic fragments have been recovered; one such in the British Museum weighs over 1400 pounds. Evidently the meteorite exploded, inflicting these singular scars upon the landscape.

Similar lakes occur on the island of Oesel in Estonia, whose "unearthly" origin has also been established by the discovery of meteoric fragments. The principal depression is occupied by a lake slightly oval, measuring 110 by 92 meters, surrounded by a rim over 18 feet in height. Five smaller oval craters, the largest more than 150 feet long, suggest that the exploding meteorite was approaching from a decided angle.

Nor need we depend upon probabilities, however convincing, for one such cluster of lakelets was imprinted upon the earth within the present century. On June 30, 1908, a huge meteorite crashed upon a lonely wilderness in Siberia, causing frightful havoc. The sound of the explosion was heard at Irkutsk, six hundred miles away, while from terrified natives came tales of blinding light and blasting heat, tales that finally filtered through to Moscow. Nearly twenty years elapsed, however, before Leonid Kulik of the Russian Academy visited the scene. Wandering on snowshoes through the Siberian winter of 1927, he finally located the site of the collision on a plateau of the Stony Tunguska, a tributary of the Yenisei. The latitude was nearly 60, the longitude about 90 East. Trees sprawled outward in every direction for a distance of thirty-seven miles from a common center, many scorched as though from the inside. They had been leveled by a blast surpassing hurricane velocity, while their charred trunks bore witness to the terrific heat of the impact. All wild life must have been annihilated. The focal point was marked by ten considerable craters from 10 to 50 meters in diameter, with scores of lesser depressions. In the largest, some 12 to 15 feet in depth, bog moss had formed, and shallow lakes have since accumulated. Had this meteorite struck the city of New York or London, the resultant chaos would have made the ravages of the atomic bomb seem minor in comparison.

A more recent display of celestial fireworks occurred on February 12, 1946, when a huge meteorite or a small asteroid, estimated to weigh a thousand tons, collided with the earth at another point in Siberia about three hundred miles northeast of Vladivostok. This voyager through space happened to be traveling in the same general direction as the earth with a velocity of about twenty miles a second. Hence there was no such terrific impact as occurred when the other great meteorite exploded over the Stony Tunguska. Nevertheless, it excavated a central crater 210 feet in diameter, while Russian savants report no fewer than 105 minor cavities caused by splinters buried in the earth over an area slightly less than two miles in length.

Meteoric pits are found in various regions: near the Henbury Cattle Station in Australia; by the legendary city of Wabar in Arabia; in Ector County, Texas. Scattered about an area of 200 square miles in South Carolina are many oval depressions, some of them 2200 feet long by 1400 wide, that may be of similar origin. Hence meteorites, though an inconsiderable factor in lake structure, offer sobering possibilities.

"VEGETATION" LAKES

In those dreary tundras where the continents of the Northern Hemisphere blend with the shallow seas, a curious type of lake abounds. Over sheets of never melting ice which mantle the frozen earth, a film of soil accumulates nourishing vegetation that renews its transient life in the brief but continuous summer sunlight. Such vegetation, interspersed with new ice strata, encloses shallow basins, creating lakes in an atmosphere soggy with moisture.

In a study of this phenomenon Robert P. Sharp observed "ground ice mounds," where such vegetation surrounded cores of ice from thirty to forty years old.

Rivers are similarly affected. Much of the broad delta of the Lena is composed of alternate layers of ice and silt, forming islands half earth, half water, which would subside below sea level were the summers ever long enough to thaw them.

Vegetation is also a factor in warmer climes. Some lakes in Argentina have been blocked out by encroaching plant life increments, as have a number of African lakes. Rivers are impeded by living dams; even the mighty Nile, in its sluggish course, is sometimes bridged by matted green growth intermingled with silt or wind-blown dust. Floating islands of earth-encrusted vegetation clog the southern reaches of Tanganyika, but such formations are evidence of the tendency of aquatic vegetation to destroy lakes rather than to create them.

Of less importance is animal intrusion into the global picture, yet many a lakelet in northern woodlands was designed by beavers as a site for their snug, half-submerged dwellings.

Their dams of felled timber, gnawed into convenient lengths and plastered with mud, arouse the admiration of human engineers. For Man himself, particularly in the past few decades, has begun to enlarge present lakes or create new ones in a far-reaching program of water conservation. But that subject deserves separate treatment later.

III

How Lakes Are Filled

RAIN, SNOW, ICE, STEAM, AND DEW

The formation of lake beds tells but half the story. How those beds have filled with water is quite as important in the economy of nature.

Many lakes received the melted residue when continental ice fields thawed and disappeared. Others were bits of ocean recaptured by wave or wind action, or uplifted rock strata. Not a few, as we shall observe, owe their origin to rivers. And there are less obvious sources of supply.

Sir John Murray estimated the annual rainfall at slightly under 30,000 cubic miles! Some evaporates, some flows into lake beds, which are natural catch basins, some seeps into the rocks to sustain that subterranean water table for which well diggers are always seeking. The upper level of this table varies widely, now gushing forth in springs, now subsiding in arid regions to such depths that even artesian wells probe for it in vain. Lakes are oftentimes its visible gauges and dry up when it recedes, as dwellers on the fringes of the great Dust Bowl have learned to their sorrow. Its presence is also revealed in subterranean rivers and sunless lakes that might otherwise reflect the stalagmites of limestone caverns. How much water lies concealed beneath the surface is conjectural. The depth to which it would flood the land, should it suddenly well upward, has been variously estimated from 29 to 914 feet. Our meager knowledge makes speculation little better than an idle groping into the unknown.

Nor is this underground ocean due solely to the rains. Some of it boils upward from the steaming interior when lowered temperatures permit those imprisoned gases, oxygen and hydrogen, to combine as H_2O. This "juvenile" water, created in the vast laboratory of the rocks, jets forth in hot springs, geysers, and volcanic vapors to add to the ocean content through passing aeons.

Sometimes the earth sips moisture directly from the atmosphere. Soil, sand, and even broken stone show this inanimate thirst. As temperatures rise, each tiny fragment collects a watery film. Chaptal estimated that during the dry season a hectare of land absorbed no less than 1700 cubic meters of water. Such invisible irrigation enables olive trees and date palms to flourish in the Sahara, where the water supply seems so inadequate. The process is called hydrogenesis and may explain the "dew ponds" of English chalk hills which, farmers aver, "drink from the air."

Although our lakes, in contrast with the oceans, hold but a fraction of 1 per cent of the global waters, their influence upon human welfare is incalculable. They are an integral part of the great circulatory system of that moisture which is no less essential to life upon our planet than is the blood stream to the individual. Isolated as they are from the parent seas, lakes have been likened to islands of water in oceans of land.

A DANGEROUS PARTNERSHIP

Lakes are frequently linked with rivers in a treacherous partnership in which they ultimately fall victims to the latter's aggressions. So long as oceans survive and rains descend upon the earth, we shall have rivers, but lakes are far less tenacious of life. Their origin is largely accidental, their allotted span relatively brief, their extinction foreordained. The very rivers which sustain them persist in their destruction, by methods as inexorable as the laws of mechanics. While the entering stream fills the lake basin with silt from the eroded uplands, the outlet stream, rasping a deeper channel, drains the dwindling waters. Innumerable lakes have been thus erased from the map.

Even the largest reveal this obliterative process. Tanganyika is the longest and, with one exception, the deepest of fresh-water lakes. Yet a tributary, the Russisi, has so silted up one sector that hippos have been observed wading in the shallows two miles offshore. The Caspian has no outlet to reduce the water level, already far below that of the Mediterranean, but the vast delta of the Volga advances from the north in a menacing semicircle while the smaller Terek, foaming down from the Caucasus, encroaches so rapidly that fishing villages on the shore in 1825 found themselves, thirty years later, ten miles inland.

Rivers seem most co-operative when they originate in lakes. A valley, forming a natural reservoir, overflows to start a stream on its journey to the sea. Ancient geographers shrewdly located the sources of the Nile in remote lakes fed by snows from some legendary Mountains of the Moon, an explanation later confirmed by the discovery of the vast nyanzas and towering peaks of equatorial Africa. Many similar conditions prevail. The Yenisei gains impetus from the inexhaustible reserves of Lake Baikal; the Congo from Tanganyika. Some rivers, like the Nile, draw tribute from several big lakes. The Mackenzie levies on Athabaska, Great Slave and Great Bear lakes, while the St. Lawrence, with all its majestic width and volume, is little more than a natural drain for the five Great Lakes.

On the other hand, not a few lakes are the definite handi-work of the rivers which created them. Turned inland from the sea, these empty into some depression to form a lake whose levels become stabilized when evaporation balances inflow. This seeming generosity, however, is capricious. Gradually the lake bed fills with silt, insuring such erratic gyrations as occur in the Persian Seistan, or causing extraordinary pulsations like those of Urmia in the same country, alternately swollen by flood and shrunken by drought. Feeder streams may shift their channels and, by-passing a terminal lake, condemn it to extinction. The Aral Sea is one of the most considerable bodies of inland water in the world, yet when the Oxus, one of its two main affluents, wandered off in the Middle Ages to empty into the Caspian, rumors issued from this remote region that the Aral was drying up.

River deltas may divide lakes into two or more sections, thus hastening their extinction. In Canada, Lake Claire and several lesser lakes have been filched away from larger Athabaska through the encroachments of the Peace and Athabaska rivers.

A river, flowing through a valley, may spread out to form a lake. Geneva is an expansion of the Rhone, which rushes into this Alpine gorge to emerge as the beautiful stream of southern France. Although such deep lakes may survive for ages, they, too, will disappear, victims of the rivers which created them.

More striking examples of river overflow occur in that dreary region known as the Canadian Shield. Here arrested drainage swells many a current like a varicose vein. The Churchill River, for example, is little more than a chain of lakes slopping one into another. As the channel deepens, they will shrink and be absorbed. Such elimination, though the work of ages, requires but a moment as geologists reckon time. In any case, long before another Ice Age spawns new legions of lakes, many thousands will have disappeared.

Mere enlargements should not be confused with such transient episodes as when Old Man River bursts his earthen shackles to flood the cotton fields of Mississippi. Even the more punctual overflows of the Amazon, which convert thousands of square miles of forest into a teeming swamp, or the clocklike regularity of Nilotic inundations, are not lakes but floods.

Odd lakes, common in certain regions, are those crescent pools, survivors of oxbow loops, carved by a river before it chose a more direct channel. The Mississippi has fathered a multitude of such disinherited waifs condemned to become reedy marshes and breeding places for mosquitoes.

As though in retaliation, a few strange lakes infest river basins, interfering with tributaries or, like leeches, draining the lifeblood from the parent stream. The valley of the Yangtze River is dotted with such lakes, formed by affluents to China's greatest river and partially dammed up by accumulated silt. They overflow into the river in time of flood, but in dry periods withdraw from it a vast volume of water.

Even more curious are the "parasitic" lakes Sven Hedin observed while exploring the valley of the Tarim River, which flows from Turkestan toward the western confines of China. He estimated the intake of one of these "robber" lagoons at nearly 5000 cubic feet a minute. No wonder the river, bereft of its waters, wanders through arid regions to lose itself in dismal salt swamps.

The tendency of water to flow away from, rather than into, certain rivers is also apparent in Australia, where anemic streams become so impoverished that they slink into the sands.

SALT LAKES AND FRESH

Strictly speaking, there are no fresh-water lakes. Even raindrops, in their brief descent, absorb some foreign matter from the atmosphere. Pure water—a product of the chemical laboratory—is unknown to nature.

To be sure, the solids dissolved in many rivers and lakes are excessively minute. The Amazon, hugest of rivers, shows, at Obidos, but 37 parts of foreign matter to 1,000,000 parts of water. The Plata, just above Buenos Aires, registers 91; the Columbia 92; the Hudson, some distance from the sea, 108; the Nile, just below Cairo, 119; the St. Lawrence at Montreal 148; the Mississippi at New Orleans 166; the Nelson at its mouth 180. More turbid is the Missouri, aptly called the Big Muddy, for at Kansas City its foreign content is 426 parts per 1,000,000; that of the Rio Grande at Laredo is 791. By such increments is the mineral content of the oceans perpetually increased.

Lakes may compare favorably with rivers in freshness. Onega, one of Russia's big lakes, is amazingly pure with only 49 parts of foreign matter to 1,000,000; Superior shows 56; Champlain 67; Baikal, Asia's huge natural reservoir, 69; Lake Tahoe 73; Crater Lake in Oregon 80; Victoria Nyanza 135; Moosehead Lake in Maine 145; Geneva in Switzerland 152; and Okeechobee, steaming in the Florida Everglades, 155.

The Canadian voyageur, like the African savage, classified waters by their taste. Fresh water was "fresh enough to drink"; brackish might serve in an emergency; others were either too salt or bitter. The term "fresh enough to drink," however, is elastic. Champlain has a muddy taste to the uninitiated; Tanganyika has been termed "peculiar," while in arid regions natives dip their drinking gourds into water so heavily charged with mineral as to be nauseous to Europeans. Kirghiz tribesmen in southern Russia even sample the Caspian Sea.

Between salt and alkaline the chemist draws a sharp distinction. The words need clarification, for while most persons regard salt (sodium chloride) as something to sprinkle on potatoes, this familiar mineral is one of many, such as "salts" of potassium, magnesium, calcium, and even gold.

Alkalis are less clearly distinguished. Webster tells us the term originally meant sodium or potassium carbonate, but has come to include some magnesium compounds, caustic soda and others. So much for definitions.

F. W. Clarke, in his *Data of Geochemistry*, would divide salt and bitter lakes into no fewer than nine classifications, according to the predominance of chlorides, sulphates, or carbonates in solution. He introduces another term, "bitterns," characteristic of the Dead Sea. A bittern, according to Webster, is "The bitter mother liquor that remains in saltworks after the salt has crystallized"; adding, "From it are obtained magnesium chloride and sulphate, and bromides and iodides." Differences in composition may be considerable. The Dead Sea, with only a trace of carbonates, shows 68 units of chlorides, while Silver Lake, with almost no chlorides, has 47 units of carbonates. Again, the Dead Sea has less than one unit of sulphates; Issyk-Kul in Central Asia has 56, and so on. In his ninth division Dr. Clarke places lakes rich in all three combinations which he calls "triple waters," with Lake Van in Armenia as an example. Even rivers may be salt or alkaline. The Saline River, a tributary of the Kansas, has 2624 parts of mineral to 1,000,000, while the Cheliff River in Algeria, according to L. Ville, has 6670.

No doubt the reader who finds scientific technicalities annoying would classify all lake minerals as salt, gypsum, lime, or borax. In commercial language, those are the important compounds.

A few lakes, small in area and discolored by decaying vegetation, reveal a slightly acid reaction. This is true of certain rivers, for, while organic matter accounts for little better than 3 per cent of the solids carried by the Danube, that percentage rises to nearly 60 in the Uruguay.

Lakes reflect their surroundings not only as mirrors of hill and forest, but in the composition of their waters. The mineral held in solution comes mainly from neighboring rocks. In limestone regions this may be eaten out bodily, but more frequently it is the freightage of inflowing streams. Most rivers are bearers of carbonates, but some specialize in sulphates. Saline lakes are usually found in regions underlain with sedimentary rock, which covers roughly three quarters of the land surface, while alkaline lakes are characteristic of volcanic or igneous rock.

Another, though lesser, factor in water contamination is the wind. Sambhar Lake in northwestern India is so salt that its drainage basin of 2200 square miles seemed an inadequate source. The winds supply the key to the mystery. Although Sambhar is four hundred miles from the sea, winds sweeping over the Rann of Cutch through the four summer months bear an impalpable dust from ocean spray. An analysis of the air indicates that 3000 tons of wind-driven salt are collected over the lake surface annually. Nor is this an isolated example. Many lakes in Australia are thought to renew their saline content by just such so-called cyclic salt.

How rich are lakes in dissolved mineral? The ocean is the standard, although the percentage there varies from 7 parts per 1000 in the upper Baltic to 42 in the sultry Red Sea. The Atlantic, saltiest of the oceans, with just over 35 grams of mineral matter per liter or 35,000 parts per 1,000,000, is the usual basis of comparison.

Neither the saltiest nor the most alkaline lake in the world is known. In some cases lake waters are so concentrated that they deposit mineral matter in winter. This occurs in Great Salt Lake, and particularly in that curious Caspian gulf known as the Kara Bugaz. In the Dead Sea the mineral content rises to approximately 245,000 parts per 1,000,000, or just about seven times that of the Atlantic. Lesser-known lakes are even more efficient chemical crucibles. Elton Lake in southern Russia shows 265,000 parts per 1,000,000; Tamentica lagoon in Chile

285,000; Tinetzky Lake in the Caspian region 289,000; and Red Lake in the Crimea slightly over 300,000. In that curious African depression known as Lake Katwe, the percentage rises to 310,000 or nearly nine times that of the Atlantic, while in the wind-swept plains of Turkestan or the sun-scorched interior of Australia some shallow vat of minerals may be even saltier or more alkaline than Katwe.

And so, because of incoming streams, dissolving rock strata, or even wind-borne particles certain lakes diverge more and more from their original freshness. A drying climate hastens the process, for when annual rainfalls fail to equal evaporation the dwindling waters become increasingly mineralized. As their areas diminish, the atmosphere, already deficient in moisture, grows drier yet, until lake beds rimmed with white become unsightly marshes and finally saltpans blistering in the sun. By just such a process have once larger bodies of fresh water degenerated into Great Salt Lake and the Dead Sea.

But if fresh-water lakes may grow salt, the converse is also true. The Caspian, once a part of the ocean, is so diluted with the vast influx of the Volga and lesser streams that its saline content is now scarcely a third that of the Atlantic. Other lakes show a greater variation. Onega, one of the freshest of all waters, was probably a part of the Arctic; Sweden's forested Lake Vener was an inlet of the Baltic; while Nicaragua, the Sweet Water Sea of the Spanish conquistadors, once formed a gulf of the Pacific.

And so we may conclude that all lakes are mineralized to a degree, while every one, without exception, is gradually becoming fresher or saltier or more alkaline in a global program of unending change.

EACH LAKE A WATERY WORLD

A lake, like an oak, has a normal life span. From obscure origins it develops, then passes its peak to a prolonged decline and ultimate death. Recorded history is too brief to present the life story of any considerable lake, which is determined by the surrounding terrain, climatic conditions, and water supply. But as lakes show every stage of development or decline, some estimate of their age is possible.

The multitude which are mere remnants of the continental ice fields seem roughly dated. Geologists believe that the glacial age went into eclipse about twenty thousand years ago and was pretty well liquidated during the following eleven millenniums.

Lakes of other origin offer more difficult problems. Baikal is a presumed product of Jurassic times, a hoary antiquity measured by tens of millions of years. The Caspian was also separated from a greater Mediterranean at a period immeasurably remote, however recent it appears on the geologist's calendar. The vast majority of lakes are comparatively recent phenomena.

Most lakes, like organisms, breathe air, which circulates throughout the entire volume. There are a few exceptions such as the Caspian, in whose profounder depths oxygen gives way to noxious hydrogen sulphide. Temperatures vary with climate and depth, deep lakes like Baikal approaching the freezing point just as do ocean abysses. Lakes are also subject to curious tremors and pulsations. Large lakes like Erie or Tanganyika may show currents suggesting the Gulf Stream, a few record perceptible tides, while many are subject to those queer oscillations known as seiches.

Lakes maintain some control over their own affairs. They remodel their outlines, carve out beaches by wave action, and distribute material in shoaling margins. Ice may add to landscape sculpturing, as when Ladoga piles layer upon layer, 70 feet deep, to drive before Arctic gales against a leeward shore.

Every lake is a miniature world which may develop a characteristic and highly specialized life. Many plants are microscopic or of that minute form known as plankton. Larger forms abound in the shallows alongshore, where the flags and rushes familiar to the Temperate Zone reach enormous size in lakes like Titicaca. Lake bottoms become coated with fine silt or soft mud, the remains of dead vegetation, which may reveal past history, just as sediments do upon the ocean floor. In his study of Scottish lakes Sir John Murray counted 277 species of plant life, a number that would be vastly multiplied throughout the lakes of the world. Sir John found animal life even more diversified, with 447 species. There was an absence of phosphorescent forms so abundant in the sea, while entire groups such as the starfishes were unrepresented.

Most important were the fishes. Some species are well known to sportsmen, from the familiar perch and bass to the grotesque but toothsome hornpout. The predatory types, such as pickerel and pike, are also favorites. Major articles of commerce are the whitefish and lake trout of the Great Lakes, while other species, such as the huge sturgeon of the Caspian, are quite as important elsewhere. Certain species, such as the marine herring and the salmon, hint at the sea as a former habitat. Still more significant are the seals in Baikal, which did not crawl across interminable leagues of dry land to that remote destination. Other ocean vagrants, now marooned, are the queer porpoises in Tung Ting Lake, China, and the sharks and giant sawfish that have become acclimated to Nicaragua's fresh waters.

Some lakes are veritable sanctuaries of archaic life, which

has disappeared elsewhere. Many of Baikal's crustaceans are found nowhere else, while a curious fish that lurks in its pitch-black abysses resembles those weird forms in ocean deeps. Fishes that survive in the darkness of subterranean lakes frequently become blind.

Life seems reluctant to abandon even lakes heavily saline or alkaline. Especially tenacious are the crustaceans, for a few degenerate brine shrimp even infest the waters of Great Salt Lake. Last of all are those precursors of death, the colonies of Beggiatoae bacilli, which feed upon disintegrating salts to produce that deadly hydrogen sulphide which bans all life. Eventually the curtain is rung down in waters like the Dead Sea, which deserves its name. Even birds shun its evil surface, presumably because there is nothing for them to eat. For aquatic birds are ardent lake lovers. Migratory types find lakes convenient rest stations on their seasonal pilgrimages, and not a few haunt such shores the year round.

Among other characteristic life of fresh-water lakes is the muskrat, the otter, and the mink. The beaver even constructs lakelets of his own. And yet too prolific life, particularly vegetation, is destructive, as the accumulated remains gradually fill up the bed until the lake becomes a marsh. The friendly waters that swarmed with so many animate entities are destined to become their grave. And so lacustrine life contributes to its own destruction.

DYING LAKES

From the moment of its origin a lake begins to die. Even lakes of impressive size may record a vast reduction in volume and area. The cities of Detroit and Chicago are built upon the beds of subsiding lakes, which once overflowed the landscape when

Huron mingled with Erie and Lake Michigan extended much farther to the west and south.

Many lakes have entered that stage where shoaling waters, choked with vegetation, degenerate into mere swamps. Even these have played a conspicuous role in history; for example, the Pontine Marshes near Rome whose malaria-breeding mosquitoes hastened the downfall of the Imperial City.

Marshes may be invested with an eerie but sinister beauty. Amid the gloom of cypresses draped with Spanish moss, inky pools, covered with a mosaic of green scum, harbor poisonous moccasins and other reptilian life. No less a nature lover than George Washington, however, wrote of one of these, "The so-called Dismal Swamp [between Virginia and North Carolina] is a glorious paradise."

Marshes may develop a semiaquatic human population. The vast Pripet Marshes between Poland and Russia are a picturesque example. There, converging upon the city of Pinsk through a maze of lagoons, come flat-bottomed boats laden with the produce of innumerable islets. Customs peculiar to the region have emerged from a fog of folklore.

Marshes have also proven a refuge to people fleeing from rapacious neighbors. In the Everglades of Florida the Seminoles have preserved their tribal practices. The marsh-fringed lakes of Africa harbor less courageous natives driven from the uplands by savage marauders. Shut out by thickets of papyrus and elephant grass, from broader horizons into which they seldom venture, they become nearly as amphibious as frogs or turtles.

Lakes which are memories rather than realities are the so-called impermanent lakes. These, according to Fritz-Jaeger, while empty in the dry season, may be partially filled during the rains, either by surface waters or the upwelling of the submerged water plane. In the latter case they are almost certain to degenerate into salt pans or gypsum beds. In arid regions, unless wind-eroded, they mark the beds of lakes which have nearly disappeared. Transient and unpredictable, they still exert some influence upon soil and climate, for even a seasonal lake is better than no lake at all.

Among these recurring phenomena is that curious blotch upon the map of South America called Salar de Uyuni. South and west of Titicaca, it fills an Andean valley eighty miles wide for a hundred miles or more. Such boundaries would make it the largest lake on that continent were it really a lake instead of an all but discarded basin.

"Salar" is a Chilean term for a depression covered with scattered deposits of salt. Unbelievably hot in summer, it is rendered still less inviting by the glare of the sun. Yet such a depression may foster marshes and in times of rainfall be partially submerged under thin sheets of water. The less extensive Salar de Coipasa, farther to the north, embraces a true lake perhaps twelve miles long. Similar areas not so heavily coated with mineral are known as salinas.

Another name for such impermanent lakes is playa, a Spanish word signifying shore or strand, for however ephemeral the water content, shore beaches are well defined. The dictionary tells us that a playa is "the flat-floored bottom of an undrained basin, becoming at times a shallow lake, which, on evaporation, may leave a deposit of salt or gypsum." The former big lakes of Australia are playas, at best, if indeed they have not become entirely dry.

Still more curious are the so-called wandering lakes, which not only ebb and flow with the season but actually shift their positions. Such is the Mar Chiquita of southern Argentina, where a broad basin formed by the subsidence of surface strata is covered with grassy flats interspersed with salt lagoons. Into this dreary region the waters of the Dulce River wander about in the rainy season, seeking a resting place, settling now in one, now in another brackish pool, to evaporate in dry weather.

Still more unusual is the famous Lop Nor of Central Asia, which, according to Sven Hedin, swings like a gigantic pendulum from one lake basin to another in the Tarim River valley over a cycle of fifteen hundred years!

The final chapter is written in the beds of dead lakes which dot our uplands. In desert regions they are marked by fields of glistening salt or gypsum quite in keeping with the bones of cattle which also perished there from lack of water. In more favorable environments they may become lush meadows or fertile farms, with former shore lines etched upon the surrounding hills. With the possible exception of the Caspian, the world's largest lakes have already been broken up into smaller fragments or have entirely disappeared; examples are the great interior waters that once flooded southern Australia; Lake Agassiz northwest of Superior, which could have swallowed all five of our present Great Lakes; and vanished Ojibway, now marked by a crescent of silted upland curved around the southern reaches of Hudson Bay.

SOME EXTRAORDINARY LAKES

In a bewildering confusion where no two lakes are just alike, a few are certain to be unusual to a marked degree. Not all lakes are water—but we anticipate.

In 1825, F. C. Walcott learned from Peruvian Indians of a peculiar red lake called Laguna Colorado. He finally located it among the mountains, a sheet of salt water about 10 miles long by 5 broad. And it was red, for it swarmed with uncountable millions of minute crustaceans which great flocks of flamingos —20,000 at least—were greedily devouring. Neighboring Indians baked the flamingo eggs to barter as trade goods.

The Polish scientist, Ossendowski, observed a similar phenomenon among the curious lakes of eastern Asia, which lie between Kazak and Siberia. A coral-red band, comprised of myriads of tiny crustaceans, encircled Lake Shunet. Bathing in the shallow waters was like bobbing on a bed of quicksilver, for they flaked off the body like splintered glass, inducing skin irritation. Across the fluid surface which bent under their weight, huge tarantulas shambled about. The natives boiled these repulsive creatures to produce a sort of spider wine! In minute doses, the virulent poison was a remedy for rheumatism; in larger amounts it induced forgetfulness, and death.

In another lake, Szira-Kul, whose bitter waters were only 7 miles long by 3 broad, the explorer found a limited area where the sounding line ran out 3200 feet, or more than twice the depth of Lake Superior!

In San Domingo, Lake Enriquillo occupies the lowest part of a bowl-shaped depression 130 feet below sea level. Around its saline waters rhinoceros iguanas, largest and fiercest of the genus, excavate burrows in limestone encrusted with coral. This region was once a gulf of the Caribbean.

Boiling lakes are not uncommon in geyser fields and volcanic areas, as already noted. Lakes that freeze upon the surface are far more numerous, but some congeal clear to the bottom to become mere cakes of ice. Nordenskjöld, who first sailed around the northern coasts of Asia, observed such a lake while marooned for a winter in Siberia. To his surprise, summer heat, which thawed the ice, revived many excellent fish which he found most appetizing.

Some icy lakes never melt. Gigantic Beerenberg, which dominates desolate Jan Mayen Island in the polar sea, holds such a lake in its vast crater more than 8000 feet above the sea. Through a cleft in the wall a glacier flows down the flanks of the mountain, a frozen river from a lake of ice in the heart of a burned-out volcano!

Many small lakes never see the light of day. Immured in

limestone caves, the fishes which frequent them have sometimes become blind in the perpetual darkness.

Among lakes too salt or bitter to drink, a few of minor size are definitely poisonous, for deadly arsenic, no less than sodium and other minerals, dissolves in water.

More curious still are non-water lakes. Such is the famous asphalt pool of Trinidad. Sir Walter Raleigh, while on a gold hunt to the Spanish Main, wrote of it, "There is that abundance of stone pitch that all the shippes of the world may be therewith laden from thence, and we made triall of it in trimming our shippes to be most excellent good, and melteth not with the sunne as pitch of Norway, and therefore for shippes trading south portes very profitable."

This singular lake covers an area of about a hundred acres. Although it seems to be in slow motion like a pan of dough, a light railroad is laid across its surface to convey the pitch. This railroad, however, must be shifted every few days or be engulfed. As fast as the asphalt is removed, it seems to well up again from some subterranean source. The depth of the lake is unknown, but laborious borings two hundred feet down fail to locate bottom. A tree, believed buried for thousands of years, came to the surface in 1928, only to disappear a month later. A mastodon's tooth has also been reported.

Webster defines asphalt as a black to dark brown solid or semisolid containing bitumens, which occur in nature or is a product of refining petroleums.

Trinidad's inky mixture shows 39 per cent asphalt mingled with light oils and mineral matter. The natives call it black gold, for millions of dollars' worth have already been excavated. Geologists believe that a rock fracture leads downward to strata impregnated with bitumen which wells up endlessly. A larger but shallower pitch lake called Bermudez lies on the coast of Venezuela, across that narrow strait that Columbus named the Serpent's Mouth. The asphalt here, which may derive from a common source, is softer, with less mineral adulterant.

Similar but smaller deposits occur elsewhere. From one such in California the bones of prehistoric animals, including the formidable saber-toothed tiger, have been recovered. Caught like flies in sticky paper, they sank into the smothering mass to leave their bones for biologists to reassemble.

A scenic wonder is that lake of restless lavas that torments the crater of Kilauea in Hawaii. Called Halomaumau, or the House of Everlasting Fire, blazing geysers spout upward fifty feet, and molten billows, surging around dark, craggy islands, undermine the scoriac cliffs and sometimes emerge through a rift in the escarpment as an incandescent river. At night the view suggests a glimpse into the heart of a tortured inferno. Innumerable later observers have endorsed the statement of Admiral Charles Wilkes, who viewed this fearsome lake when he visited the islands on a sailing vessel more than a century ago. "The sight," he said, "was magnificent and worth a voyage around the world to witness."

IV

African Lakes

THE BIG LAKES OF AFRICA

Unlike North America's five Great Lakes, which extend roughly east and west for 1160 miles, have a similar history and characteristics, and empty as a unit through the St. Lawrence River, Africa's group of big lakes stretches north and south for an even greater distance, 1420 miles, and exhibits notable differences both in origin and in appearance.

Two of these big lakes, Victoria and Albert Nyanza, drain into the Nile, which also levies upon Edward, reed-choked Kioga, and Tana in Abyssinia. Their waters ultimately reach the Mediterranean.

Huge Tanganyika, receiving the overflow from Lake Kivu, spills spasmodically into the Congo, which also stems from Mweru and marshy Bangweulu. It flows into the South Atlantic.

Nyasa, deep and commodious, with a number of lesser associates, turns southward to connect with the Zambezi and the Indian Ocean.

Rudolf, another of the world's big lakes, has a drainage basin of its own, as does that lacustrine curiosity, Rukwa, and better-known Magadi and Natron.

Most of these lakes lie along that stupendous crack in the earth's surface known as the Great African Rift. Some were formed when rock strata were torn asunder or caved in. Others fill broad and relatively shallow depressions in the undulating surface. Hence, while Tanganyika is nearly a mile

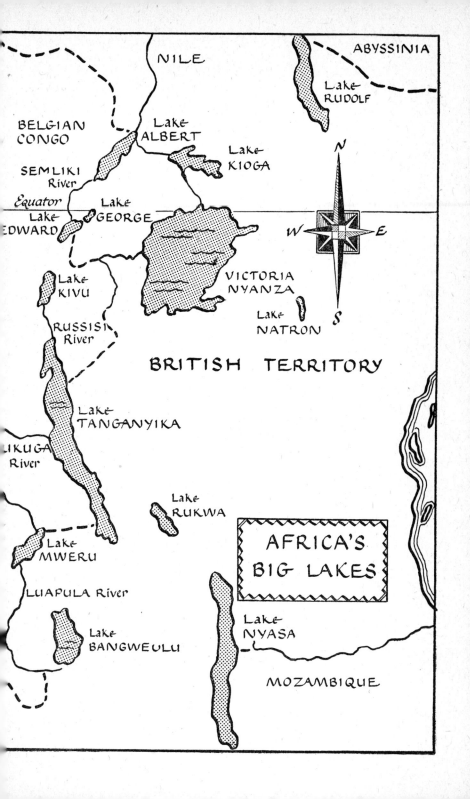

deep, Kioga and Bangweulu rarely exceed fifteen feet, while
that soda-caked curiosity, Magadi, has a reported depth of only
a few inches.

The surrounding terrain is quite as varied and complex:
alternate desert, forest, broken by broad tablelands 8000 feet
high, smoking volcanoes, and the loftiest mountains on the
continent.

Some of these lakes are of rare beauty, their surfaces
adorned with islands of enchanting loveliness. Others are
rimmed with sun-baked rock and sand, as lifeless as the Sahara.
Some are vast reservoirs of sweet water; others are brackish;
still others intensely saline. A few are so impregnated with
minerals as to be definitely poisonous.

Rosy flamingos haunt these lakes, together with numberless
storks, ibises, and other quaint and picturesque birds. Crocodiles infest their marshy shores, where hippos wallow con-
tentedly in the mud.

Many tribes inhabit their coastal regions. Some, like the
peace-loving dwellers in Uganda, have evolved a culture with
villages, flocks, herds, cultivated gardens, and a crude native
currency. In contrast are the ferocious cannibals of Tanganyika, the semiaquatic Pariahs who lurk in Albert's marshes,
and the almost simian types that peer furtively from the
forests about Lake Kivu.

Since immemorial times these lakes have been navigated
by native craft ranging from clumsy dugouts to elaborately
carved and ornamented war canoes. Through the Middle Ages
blunt Arab dhows sailed where steamers and even modern
gunboats now proclaim the superior civilization of the white
man.

The big lakes of Africa! Since remote antiquity they have
been pictured in legend, but only within recent decades has
the dark curtain been lifted from a region so fascinating and
rich in promise.

A GIGANTIC EARTH CRACK

The earth's most colossal fracture stretches from western Asia far down the African continent. It was first recognized in Syria and Palestine. To explain the Jordan River trough, which reaches its nadir in the abyss of the Dead Sea, geologists were led to trace a prolonged crack in the rock strata. Professor Hull, in 1889, found that limestone layers overlying Mount Hor reappeared at its base 5000 feet below. The discovery of Lake Rudolf a year earlier had led Professor Suess to suspect a continuation of this huge crevice along the bed of the Red Sea, thence inward by a lake-marked chasm through Abyssinia's mountains toward interior Africa. In places the subsidence was profound, approaching 11,000 feet in the Red Sea basin.

Professor J. W. Gregory seems to have been the first to name this titanic fissure the Great African Rift. Other investigators traced it southward until it swerves toward the Indian Ocean in Portuguese East Africa, more than five thousand miles from its northernmost point in the Lebanon Mountains.

There are really three great rifts through much of the African sector, extending generally north and south.

The westernmost is the deepest and most recent. In places along the shores of Tanganyika its edge is marked by cliffs thousands of feet high. Elsewhere prolonged erosion has smoothed down once jagged escarpments, particularly where the displacement was not so pronounced.

In this cracking up and splitting asunder of the earth surface great areas were blocked out and subsided, while other areas rose above the continental level. Hence, along the Rift edges have reared the loftiest mountains in Africa, topped by Kilimanjaro, 19,321 feet high and snow-capped under the Equator. Other towering peaks are the Ruwenzori range, 16,749 feet high, the formidable Kenya mass, isolated Mount Elgon, and the still smoking craters of the Mfumbiro volcanoes.

The entire region illustrates the play of tectonic forces in lake structure. What happened more than a century ago at New Madrid in Tennessee, when Reelfoot Lake was born, has been here enacted upon a colossal scale for millions of years. Deep earth cracks and blocked-out masses have formed the beds for Africa's most capacious lakes. Nor has the grand drama been completed, for several of these lakes have undergone momentous changes during recorded history, and some are still in a state of cataclysmic growth or destruction.

Across the three main Rift valleys stretch many transverse fractures which complicate the picture. The bed of Lake Nyasa is a convergence of several such. The whole region presents a complex problem to the geologist with many details still unsolved.

THE STORIED NILE

Although the Nile nurtured perhaps the most ancient of civilizations, it remained for thousands of years a river of mystery. The priests of Egypt, viewing its annual overflow with superstitious reverence, worshiped it as a God, for its silt brought inexhaustible fertility. The narrow belt of verdure was all the more conspicuous because of the deserts which flanked it on either hand. Hence Egypt, with its grandiose creations, its obelisks, sphinxes, and pyramids, its palaces, its temples, and its tombs, was, in the poetic vernacular of the time, "the gift of the Nile."

Herodotus, lured by insatiable curiosity, sailed up the Nile to the first cataract in 457 B.C. and speculated about the river's origin. Aristotle thought it rose in the Silver Mountains. Eratosthenes, librarian at Alexandria, who first measured the circumference of the earth, hinted at equatorial lakes as a probable source. An expedition sent by Nero to investigate was stopped by impassable swamps. Diogenes, a Greek merchant on the Indian Ocean, somewhere about A.D.50, reported a toilsome inland journey of twenty-five days, and two great lakes which were "the source of the Nile." Ptolemy drew a map placing these lakes in the interior, fed by melted snows from lofty peaks which he called the "Mountains of the Moon." Arab adventurers of the Middle Ages mentioned mysterious lakes in the African hinterland. Leonardo da Vinci wrote of the Nile, "It is known that it issues from the Mountains of the Moon by several unexplained sources," adding, "We must conclude those mountains to be of the greatest height upon which clouds, falling in snow, give rise to the Nile."

Such explanations, though reasonably accurate, were confirmed less than a century ago by explorers: British officers in the employ of the East India Company, traders, and missionaries. Among the former were John Speke and Captain James Grant, whose names survive in species of African antelopes. Noteworthy also were Sir Richard Burton and Sir Samuel Baker. David Livingstone, the great missionary, was groping for the ultimate source of the Nile when he fell victim to deadly fever in the marshes of Bangweulu. Henry Stanley and others added much information.

The big lakes so long hidden beyond the horizon of scientific certainty have been identified as Victoria Nyanza, Albert Nyanza, and lesser associates. The fabled Mountains of the Moon are presumably the Ruwenzori range, although possibly Kenya or gigantic Kilimanjaro may have been indicated, while the great river itself has been ascended to its remotest tributary.

Two main branches unite to form the Nile. The lesser in length, though often the more copious in flood, is called the Blue Nile, rising in the tangled mountain peaks of Abyssinia and bearing the overflow from Lake Tana. The longer branch, known as the White Nile, has its principal source in Victoria, the second most extensive body of fresh water in the world. Its "farthest south" is reached in the Kagera River, which empties into this great lake. From the headwaters of the Kagera to the many-branching delta on the Mediterranean coast the Nile meanders northward for 4037 miles. So narrow is the drainage basin, however, that its area is substantially less than that of the Congo, swollen with the rains of the equatorial forest.

On its leisurely course, which may be said to traverse Victoria Nyanza, the river emerges as the Victoria Nile, spilling over a 16½-foot declivity at Ripon Falls. Losing itself for a time in shallow Lake Kioga, with its endless marshes, it proceeds northward to plunge through a rocky cleft only 18 feet wide for a sheer drop of 120 feet at Murchison's Falls. Some twenty miles distant it empties into another great lake, Albert Nyanza, whence it reappears as the White Nile. Flowing sluggishly once more, it crosses an extensive territory one third as large as the British Isles, the famous Nile Sudd. Here the pistia, or Nile cabbage, and other aquatic plants flourish in such profusion that they clog the channel. Great floating masses, collecting like the floe ice of the Arctic, form peatlike bridges firm enough to support an elephant. Papyrus and elephant grass twenty feet high add to the all but impenetrable tangle. Through this living barricade boats must dredge a channel by dragging anchorlike implements equipped with saw teeth. Escaping from this jungle prison in the African uplands, the Nile descends by a series of steplike cataracts in the Egyptian Sudan and Egypt proper to pursue its way between lofty battlements that resemble the palisades of the Hudson.

Across such a varied terrain of huge lakes, snowy mountains, foaming cascades, and aquatic jungles, the storied river at length wins its way outward to the sea.

REGAL VICTORIA

Some four hundred miles from the Indian Ocean, its northern sector cut by the Equator, lies the most expansive of Africa's big lakes. Its area, 26,200 square miles, exceeds that of any other body of fresh water in the world, except Superior. Quite in keeping with its size is its name, half Latin, half aboriginal —Victoria Nyanza.

Roughly oblong, its major axis stretches from southwest to northeast for more than 250 miles. Its extreme width is about 160. The shore line of over 2000 miles is broken by many indentations. Kavirondo Gulf on the northeast, 50 miles long and nearly landlocked by rocky peninsulas and islands, has become slightly brackish. Speke Gulf to the southeast is even more commodious. Kienda (Ninety) Bay on the southwestern corner is so named because ninety natives perished there when two war canoes capsized.

Victoria had its origin in early Pleistocene times. Although in the sphere of the Rift fractures, it is not, like most other African big lakes, the result of tectonic action. It fills a broad and relatively shallow basin in a tableland 3720 feet above the sea. Its drainage basin of 92,000 square miles was once occupied by a more extensive lake that, according to L. S. Leakey, was three hundred feet deeper.

This inland sea may have drained into the Congo. If so, its outlet had shifted to the Nile long before the builders of the Pyramids began to wonder just where the muddy waters swirling past came from. The western shores are low, the lake bed gently shelving. On the south, however, a steep escarpment appears in cliffs 300 feet high. The maximum depth is usually given as 270 feet, while many submerged shoals are continually coming to light, but Dr. Felix Oswald, in 1912, reported one point not far from the eastern coast where his sounding line had run out 250 fathoms without touching bottom.

E. G. Ravenstein, who studied fluctuations in the water levels, decided that these had varied over ten feet in twenty years. He also suspected tides and seiches.

Although Victoria was vaguely known to the ancients and probably visited by Arab traders in the Middle Ages, John Speke was the first European of record to sight its strangely beautiful surroundings. On the shores of Tanganyika, where he had gone with Sir Richard Burton in 1858, he learned from an Arab of a larger lake, "so broad that you could not see across it and so long that nobody knew its length." Eager to verify this report, Speke journeyed through an unknown region until, from a gentle slope, there burst upon his gaze "the vast expanse of the pale blue waters of the Nyanza."

Speke was enchanted. He thought the countryside quite as attractive as an English landscape. Before him spread an extensive archipelago, each island a single hill clothed in verdure. Beyond shimmered "the distant sea line of the northern horizon in the calm atmosphere."

He questioned the natives, but they could tell him only that the "lake reached to the ends of the earth." Tasting its waters, he found them sweet, though not so palatable as those of Tanganyika, a judgment which later visitors have questioned. He described them as a "dirty white," and was struck by the myriads of mosquitoes which covered the vegetation in a "perfectly marvelous" manner. Then remembering that he was an officer of the East India Company and a loyal subject of Her Majesty, he named his discovery Victoria—"nyanza" being the native word for lake.

Speke was anxious to explore the northern section, which he thought was crossed by the Equator (a correct surmise), but dwindling trade goods forbade. Four years later he returned better equipped. This time he located the outlet, now called the Victoria Nile, and traced the Great River through much of its course all the way to Egypt. The riddle that had baffled the Sphinx was solved at last.

Henry M. Stanley first circumnavigated the lake in 1874, while more recent surveys have defined its boundaries. The surrounding terrain is varied and pleasing. About fifty miles from the northwestern shore Mount Elgon rears its tremendous crater over 14,000 feet. Around its wide sweeping flanks the caves where natives once stabled their flocks are alive with bats and fleas!

Many aboriginal tribes inhabit the coastal regions. In Uganda they developed a culture of their own with settled communities which enjoyed a considerable prosperity. The waters of the lake abound with fish, while hippos and particularly crocodiles are numerous. Oddly enough, one island called Godsiba, near the middle of the lakes, seems free from these repulsive reptiles.

Since the days of Speke, visitors have never ceased to admire Victoria's islands. From mere rocks they range upward to an area of 170 square miles. Some are grassy, some forested, some fringed with white beaches. A few are guano-smeared blocks, the nesting place of countless birds. Buvuma has an irregular outline suggesting Celebes; Ukerewe, in the southern part, is 25 miles long by 12 broad. Some islands were dedicated to savage rites in which human sacrifices appeased the wrath of the lake god when his fierce winds lashed the waters to frenzy. Now his temples are deserted and the islands swallowed up by the jungle. For an unspeakable horror has settled like a pall over great sections of the lake shore in that dread sleeping sickness whose ravages recall the visitations of the Black Death in the Middle Ages. On some of the islands from 1901–06, the mortality rose to 428 per 1000.

The causative agent is a minute protozoan burdened with the rather formidable name of *Trypanosoma gambiense*, which is distantly related to the germ of syphilis. The carrier is the tsetse fly, *Glossina palpalis*, which infests marshy lowlands and shrubbery. The protozoan, introduced into the blood stream by the bite of this fly, gradually invades the tissues. The disease runs a characteristic course over a period of about two years, until increasing lethargy and drowsiness culminate in the sleep of death. Two thirds of the natives in Uganda succumbed, while the mortality over much of the Belgian Congo was equally alarming. In French Equatorial Africa Dr. Frantzen estimated that 6,000,000 people had perished during a period of eight years.

To combat the scourge, the government removed whole populations from stricken areas. But the poor natives, dying by the thousands, wandered back to their ancestral shores, although this meant almost certain death. The installation of tsetse fly traps, the clearing away of brush, vaccination, and improved methods of treatment are gradually bringing the terrible malady under control.

Meanwhile, not all the coastal regions have fallen under its baleful shadow. Railways from the seacoast now converge upon Victoria, and steamers maintain regular sailings over routes once pre-empted by fishing dugouts and gaudily decorated war canoes. The plateau is essentially healthy even for Europeans, while the lake in the foreground is a perpetual challenge to the white man's enterprise.

LESSER NILOTIC LAKES

1. KIOGA

The Nile, bursting out of Victoria Nyanza over the foaming spillway of Ripon Falls, soon enters a weird region of papyrus and elephant grass, of shallow pools and soggy marshlands, where its current becomes so retarded that at times it ceases altogether or is actually reversed. Here it overflows to create that curiosity among lakes known as Kioga.

This mingling of mud banks and sluggish waterways stretches from east to west across Uganda for over 120 miles. In some places it attains a width of 25 or 30 miles, but its contours are so formless and shifting that surveys are well-nigh impossible.

On the map Kioga resembles one of those reservoirs where the damming of a river has forced the water to back up into lateral depressions, giving somewhat the appearance of a distorted centipede. Nature here followed the same procedure in her more leisurely way, for an upheaval of the earth crust imprisons the river for a time in a semiaquatic jungle.

The waters of Kioga, seldom over fifteen feet deep, are usually much more shallow. In places they present an undulating meadow of hyacinths starred with giant lotus blossoms that burden the air with sticky fragrance. But there is also a poisonous miasma, suggestive of endemic fever, that curse of tropic countries. Birds by the millions haunt the reedy fens where crocodiles sun themselves on steaming banks and hippos luxuriate in the shallows. The silence is aquiver with the hum of innumerable insects and pierced by the shrill call of birds. The half-submerged shores blend imperceptibly with the waters, which seem undecided whether to be a lake or a swamp and have become a confused mixture of both.

No estimate of Kioga's area is better than a speculative guess. But if it does not rank among the big lakes of the world, it is certainly one of the most unusual.

2. Albert Nyanza

West and a bit north of Kioga lies another lake which unquestionably belongs among the big lakes, as its area is 1640 square miles. Sir Samuel Baker and his wife were the first Europeans to glimpse its enchanting scenery. In 1864, from a precipitous cliff, they gazed out across its pale blue waters to the formidable Rift escarpment in the distance, rising 2000 feet or more, with loftier headlands beyond.

Sir Samuel was a prince among explorers. Huge of frame, with a leonine countenance, the natives called him the Lion's Mane; his wife, the Daughter of the Moon. Both were much beloved and when stricken with fever were cared for with the utmost devotion.

Seeking the headwaters of the Nile, they had stumbled upon one of its vast interior reservoirs. Sir Samuel wrote, "We are about 1500 feet above the lake and I looked down from the steep granite cliff where, like a sea of quicksilver . . . lay the grand expanse of water. . . . It is impossible to describe the triumph of that moment."

The Englishman named his new-found lake for Albert, late husband of Queen Victoria. It lies in the western fracture of the Great Rift, at an elevation of 2037 feet, and is 100 miles long by 22 wide. Its shallow waters nowhere seem to exceed fifty feet in depth. Quite recently, perhaps within historic time, a much larger lake filled the depression to a depth of a thousand feet or more.

The extraordinary shrinkage seems due mainly to tectonic

changes, for the same forces which caused the Rift are still
active, particularly in remoter regions to the south and west.
Albert shows extensive faulting, as though an earthenware
bowl had cracked on the sides to allow the contents to drain
away. Climatic changes may also be affecting both the influx
of water and the rate of evaporation, while the two great rivers
that discharge into the lake are rapidly completing its destruction by their deposits of silt.

The resultant shrinkage is only too apparent. The considerable island of Nyamsasi which greeted visitors in 1889 is now
a peninsula, as are other former islands, while farther offshore
many shoals emerge as new islets.

The Victoria Nile, bearing the waters of that vast nyanza,
enters the northeastern end of the lake through a fan-shaped
delta which continually advances. Here the shores, already
constricted, narrow still more, while a perceptible current sets
northward, increasing as the waters pour into the Bahr el Jebel
or Mountain River, better known as the White Nile. At its
southern extremity Albert receives another river, the Semliki,
through a papyrus swamp scarcely three feet deep. Farther
upstream the original lake bed is now an alluvial plain. Soon,
as geologists reckon time, Albert seems destined to become a
swamp and then a fertile valley where two rivers join.

Volcanic disturbances appear in hot springs and geysers.
Salt springs gush from the soil, particularly during the dry
season. In certain localities petroleum seeps out. Yet the lake
waters are fresh, fed as they are by two big rivers, while
numerous other streams come cascading down the western
escarpment, broken by many rugged ravines which lead back
into the high tableland.

This shore line is marked by the formidable cliffs of the Rift
fracture, but the eastern, more low-lying, is deeply etched by
lagoons separated by sandy points. Here natives construct
rude traps or nets for the giant Nile perch, which occasionally

attains a weight of 200 pounds. Turtles that tip the scale at a hundred are also fairly numerous.

Albert has a drainage basin of about 16,000 square miles. The Semliki, a tributary of the Nile system, bends in a great semicircle for 160 miles around the massive Ruwenzori range, the fabled Mountains of the Moon. The snows that crown its jagged sky line, 16,794 feet high, drain into the Semliki, which is further swollen by torrents sweeping down from the Congo tableland, clothed with forests unmatched anywhere else on earth save in the valley of the Amazon.

As Albert forms part of the boundary between Uganda and the Belgian Congo, it falls under the jurisdiction of both Great Britain and Belgium. To complete the geographical picture, we need to follow the Semliki to even stranger lakes which lie beyond.

3. LAKES EDWARD AND GEORGE

Lake Edward, source of the Semliki River, was discovered in 1889 by Henry M. Stanley, who was also the first white man of record to gaze upon the tremendous ramparts of the Ruwenzori. That imposing panorama is often obscured, however, by a mist that hovers over the surface of the lake.

This surface lies at an elevation of 3004 feet above sea level, and is 44 miles long by 32 broad. The waters, though somewhat brackish, abound with fish; crocodiles and hippos are also plentiful. A swampy plain, once part of the lake bed, is the site of several salt pans and steaming geysers. Here and there cliffs 300 feet high trace the edge of the Rift. A winding channel 25 miles long connects with a smaller lake known to the natives as Dweru, but rechristened George in further honor of the royal family. This water, 20 miles long by 10 in width, is cut by the Equator. The two lakes have a combined area of 820 square miles.

Still stranger lakelets along the northeastern shores of Edward occupy burned-out craters or caldera caused by internal gaseous explosions. Most noteworthy is Katwe, which is separated from its big companion by a rocky rim only 160 feet thick. Its rose-red surface, dark crimson in the shadows, contrasts strangely with Edward's pale green. Although the waters of Katwe are scarcely four feet deep, they hold in solution an estimated 400,000 tons of mineral. The pure salt which continuously separates in crystals upon the surface is an important article of commerce.

Like Albert, Edward is shallow, although Worthington found one depression over 350 feet deep.

The natives of the district and the neighboring Semliki Valley are as unusual as their surroundings. In the latter dwell the Batwa or Bambuta pygmies, whose height seldom exceeds four feet nine inches. They have long upper lips and almost bridgeless noses. Extremely fond of honey, they track wild bees to their hidden storehouses. Their chief defense is an uncanny knowledge of the forests and the possession of poison arrows. Like most primitive peoples, they love music and are adept at drawing. Their rudimentary beliefs involve little save fear of thunderstorms and a nebulous notion that the soul of the departed enters the body of the red bush pig.

Ewart Grogan, who approached the lake from the western hinterland, found that the old bed exceeded the present one by at least a hundred and twenty square miles. In places it was punctured by pits of flame and jets of steam.

The Ruchuru River, which discharges into Edward from the south, is slightly brackish. It is of interest because it marks the uttermost headwaters of the Nile in this region of Africa, and was probably once the outlet of that amazing lake called Kivu, now shut off by a group of formidable volcanoes.

Amid the papyrus swamps in the delta of the Ruchuru, Grogan found a tribe of wretched natives who lived a semiaquatic life. Sheltered by reedy thickets from more aggressive tribes, they seldom ventured from their marshy fastnesses.

For some years Edward was closed to the outside world by government edict, as medical science strove to control the ravages of sleeping sickness.

AMAZING LAKE KIVU

In a remote depression of the Great Western Rift, shut out from its former outlet to Lake Edward by still flaming volcanoes, lies Kivu. Called the most beautiful lake in Africa, it has been described by Grogan, who visited it around 1900, as "a blend of Scotland, Japan, and the South Sea Islands."

The lake lies wholly in the Belgian Congo, about midway between Edward to the north and Tanganyika to the south. Elevated nearly a mile above sea level or, to be exact, 4829 feet, its length is 62 miles, its extreme width over 30. The surface is dotted by a maze of islands that Grogan thought must number at least a thousand. One of these, called by the natives Kwic Hui or Kwijwi, lofty and rugged, is 22 miles long.

The waters of Kivu are, to say the least, peculiar. Though deep and usually clear, they suddenly change from blue and green to purple and gray. While the air remains calm, they may all at once become furiously agitated and filled with sediment. Oily patches appear, accompanied by the odor of hydrogen sulphide. In certain areas bubbling hot springs make them uncomfortably warm for swimmers, while boric acid crusts the rocks with white. H. F. Wollaston claimed the waters were salt, and they do contain much mineral matter in solution..

The fires of creation which smolder about Lakes Albert and Edward are here in a state of violent activity and the very earth crust seems plastic and changing. In Grogan's apt phrase, the "whole territory between Kivu and Edward still bubbles" —a striking example of lake structure by volcanic action.

Around the northern end of Kivu and blocking off all egress in that direction, tower the Mfumbiro volcanoes. They were probably sighted in the blue distance by Stanley and possibly by Speke. Two huge craters obstruct the Rift valley, the loftier, Karasimbi, rearing 14,780 feet above the sea. Six other great cones are grouped about the lake, three on one side, three on the other. All have been recently active, while two have been observed by Europeans in the very throes of eruption.

Grogan was informed by the natives that recent lavas had cut off a herd of frightened elephants. In confirmation he stumbled upon the skeleton of one of these wretched animals. Von Boringe, with a German expedition in 1902, found that the lavas had set neighboring forests on fire. The whole northern shore of the lake is rimmed by lava flows and volcanic ash.

Kivu was discovered in 1894 by Count Götzen, for at that time it lay upon the farther border of the German province of Tanganyika. The Duke of Mecklenburg, who surveyed the lake in 1908, lost two canoes with their native paddlers, while crossing the northern sector.

In this wild region several species of animals, rare elsewhere, have found a protective environment. Into the vast Congo forests to the west Sir Harry Johnson tracked that striped enigma, the okapi, sole relative of the giraffe, perhaps the shyest of all animals, and previously unknown. Captain J. E. Phillips found gorillas high on one of the dormant volcanoes, and also observed two hippos wading in the Kivu shallows, although previous observers had reported that these ungainly animals, as well as crocodiles, were wholly absent.

Human life seems quite in keeping with the uncanny terrain. The gloomy forests harbor two races of pygmies, one jet-black, the other reddish brown. Strangest of all are the apelike creatures that steal furtively from the forest. Though much taller than the pygmies, the latter treat them with contempt. Other natives, even the lowest tribes, call them Banande and regard them as pariahs. They have been described as definitely simian, with short legs, enormously elongated arms, prognathous jaws, and slant foreheads, while their bodies are notably hairy. They seemed apprehensive, as though they had just stepped into a hostile world from the Neolithic Age. Later travelers have verified the presence of these queer "missing links" on the outskirts of primitive society.

Kivu's rising waters, barred from their northern outlet into Lake Edward and the Nile by the still heaving and tumultuous earth, have forced an exit southward through the Russisi River, evidently of recent geological origin, to empty into Tanganyika.

Various lesser lakes sprinkle the mountainous terrain or lurk in the shadow of the awesome Congo forest. Some are crater lakes in extinct volcanoes, others much larger though presumably of volcanic origin. Mrs. Patrick Ness, who penetrated into this singular region from the Nile Valley in 1928, was impressed with Bunyoni, the "lake of the little birds." Sixteen miles long and studded with islands, it seemed abloom with blue water lilies. Some of these lakes are said to mirror tropic vegetation of almost unreal beauty, but none is so strange or fascinating as Kivu itself, in its weird setting, so newly forged and fashioned by volcanic fires.

ABYSMAL TANGANYIKA

The western fracture of the African Rift is etched upon a contour map in that chain of lakes which fills its deepest depressions. This fracture stretches roughly north and south, through

a flattened arc of some 900 miles. At the northern tip lies
Albert Nyanza, followed in turn by Lakes Edward and Kivu.
But roughly one half, and much the deepest portion, is occu-
pied by Tanganyika.

There is a barbaric cadence in that name which is highly
appropriate. Across its emerald-green waters, guarded by
cliffs that rise in places more than half a mile, are mirrored the
lights and shadows of the Dark Continent. Here scenes of
almost unreal beauty are marred by man's inhumanity to man;
for upon its shores bloodthirsty cannibals once dwelt, and
Arab slave dealers plied their infamous traffic. Sleeping sickness also takes its grisly toll of human life.

Tanganyika is the longest of all fresh-water lakes. The
jagged crevice which it occupies slices through mountainous
terrain for 450 miles. This is a hundred miles longer than Lake
Superior. Its width, however, nowhere exceeds 45 miles. Its
area, 12,700 square miles, gives it high rank among the world's
great lakes, in ninth place at least; perhaps eighth, in view of
the indefinite surveys of its closest rival, Great Bear Lake in
upper Canada.

A clearer understanding of its relative importance is revealed
by its abysmal soundings. Throughout most of its sinuous
course Tanganyika's depth is impressive. In the southern sector Dr. Louis Stappers, in 1912, found a depth of 4708 feet,
only a few hundred feet short of a mile. Besides being the
longest of fresh-water lakes, it is, except Baikal in Asia, also
the deepest. Although it lies at an elevation of 2536 feet, its
profoundest gulfs penetrate nearly 2000 feet below sea level.
No accurate computation of its volume has yet been made,
but there is some reason to believe that it holds more water
than Lake Superior. Certainly it is much more voluminous than
its sprawling neighbor, Victoria Nyanza, and almost justifies
Stanley's descriptive phrase, that "fathomless gulf."

Tanganyika was known to the Arabs for centuries, before

Burton and Speke, first among Europeans, visited it in 1858. Traveling overland from Zanzibar, they reached Ujiji, the principal lake port, only to succumb to native maladies. Burton, prostrated by fever, expected to die, but ultimately recovered. Speke, nearly blinded by ophthalmia, suffered a temporary facial paralysis when a beetle, crawling into his ear, caused a dangerous infection. But he haunted the native bazaars, tried vainly to hire an Arab dhow, then set off in two canoes, hollowed out of logs, to explore the northern sector. He found the country alive with elephants, rhinos, and lions, and encountered one herd of savage buffalo. Marshy districts swarmed with hippos and crocodiles, and the waters teemed with fish. He passed safely through a belt of tsetse flies, then imperfectly understood, prudently avoided the Wakembe cannibals, and observed along the northwestern shores stupendous cliffs 2000 feet high, the raw edge of the exposed Rift. It was at Tanganyika that he first heard of Victoria, which he was later to discover and name. As the explorers were seeking the headwaters of the Niles, Speke turned to the right track. Burton, however, remained obstinately certain that Tanganyika was the sought-for source. The two men quarreled, drifted apart, and became enemies. Both, however, were courageous and sincere, and their differences are forgotten in the light of notable achievement.

Some years later Ujiji was the scene of a global news feature. The great missionary, David Livingstone, had disappeared into the unknown hinterland. James Gordon Bennett, publisher of the New York *Herald*, then commissioned one of his star news hawks, Henry M. Stanley, to find the missing man. After a hazardous search of 235 days, Stanley reached Ujiji November 10, 1871. There he found a white-haired stranger, wasted with fever, seated under a mango tree. Extending his hand, he remarked, "Dr. Livingstone, I presume?" The mango tree has gone, but a monument marks the spot.

Livingstone, true to his scientific instincts, had already made important observations. He noted that a current set north from February to November, turning southward through the balance of the year. These movements, he thought, were caused by unequal rainfall and evaporation, and he ascribed to them the sweetness of the waters.

When his health was restored, Livingstone accompanied Stanley on an exploring tour to the north. Far better equipped than Speke, they observed the same towering cliffs and found a river entering the northern end of the lake through a delta much impeded by reeds. This is the Russisi flowing southward from Lake Kivu. Grogan, who explored it later, claimed that the river had silted up sixty miles of ancient lake bed and was still encroaching upon the present lake through its five mouths.

Livingstone also explored the southern end of Tanganyika. Along its eastern shore he found many indentations forming broad lagoons four or five miles long and so choked with aquatic growth that a canoe could hardly force an entrance. The extreme southern coastline proved to be a great natural bowl whose precipitous sides were smothered with vegetation.

In 1874 English Lieutenant Verney Lovett Cameron made a survey of this region, traveling in canoes with native paddlers. He described the southernmost cliffs as "resembling ruined battlements, clothed with verdure, draped with gigantic vines and creepers, and alive with monkeys." It was a scene so wildly beautiful that he wrote, "One might expect to see fairies emerge from such grottoes." Most curious of all were the floating islands. These had their foundations in dense growths of cane grass which became matted with other vegetation. In time a peaty surface formed, in which all manner of plant life was rooted. Breaking loose from natural holdfasts, these living gardens drifted off before the winds to present a moving landscape. Similar rank growth obstructed incoming streams or bridged their currents with almost solid archways.

Proceeding halfway up the unexplored western coast, Cameron came upon a break in the Rift escarpment more than a mile wide, through which the lake seemed to be slopping over into a broad channel scarcely three feet deep. Down this channel he fought his way through smothering vegetation for five miles or more, until further progress was effectually barred. Here soundings showed a depth of 18 feet. At first Cameron was in doubt as to whether he had found an outlet or a tributary, but he inclined to the former opinion, because the shores were clogged with tree trunks and other debris from the forested lake. This queer river, known to the natives as the Lukuga, proved even queerer than its first appearance seemed to warrant. For subsequent examination revealed that it marked the bed of an ancient stream that once flowed into Tanganyika but had silted up and been left high and dry by the collapse of the Rift floor.

When Cameron observed it, the Lukuga was evidently undecided in which direction to flow. Stanley later found no perceptible current. But in 1878, according to M. Theeuws, the rising lake waters finally forced an outlet through this ancient valley, dredging out the silted bottom. If his conclusions are correct, we have here a picture of a vast lake forcing an outlet after prolonged isolation.

As if in confirmation, lake levels subsided. Ujiji's ancient harbor, once crowded with canoes and dhows, became dry land, while the lake settlement of Karema was left a mile inland.

The Lukuga and Tanganyika may be considered the headwaters of the Congo, although other branches of that great river penetrate farther to the south.

Cameron found the waters of Tanganyika fresh but with a brackish taste at times. The huge lake is so deep that it shows some tendency to become stagnant through lack of circulation, for there are few tributaries, while the outlet, as above noted, has been indefinite and intermittent.

Other explorers have shed further light on this interesting region. Major Hotine conducted a triangulation survey of a considerable stretch of eastern shore line around Mount Kungwe, looming up to a height of 4723 feet. He encountered numerous crocodiles and a few lions, listened to the incantations of witch doctors and the throb of drums, observed many fishing canoes with nets drying in the sun, and safely traversed another belt of the dreaded tsetse flies. Long stretches of coast line are now cleared of brush in an effort to combat that deadly carrier of sleeping sickness.

A biological survey conducted about 1900 gave rise to the so-called Tanganyika problem. The discovery in its waters of certain ganoid fishes, marine mollusks, and at least one species of jellyfish suggested a former connection with the ocean. A sharp cleavage of opinion followed with few facts to go upon.

Sir Alfred Sharpe examined the western shores in 1911–12. He crossed a lofty tableland in places 8000 feet high, comprising grassy slopes interspersed with patches of scrub, and thought the great lake extremely beautiful.

Most of Tanganyika's western shore line lies in the Belgian Congo. There the only prominent indentation, Burton Gulf, projects inland like the barb on a native spear. Toward the south the big lake touches northern Rhodesia, while much of the eastern coast borders what was once the German province of Tanganyika, now under British control.

A railroad from Dar-es-Salaam on the Indian Ocean connects with Ujiji, a miniature Zanzibar with a population rising 25,000. A branch of this railroad strikes northward to the southern shore of Victoria Nyanza.

Steamers now ply waters once given over to dugout canoes and Arab dhows. Someday, no doubt, this vast natural reservoir will fulfill the dream of Arab slavers who called it the gateway to Central Africa.

LOTUS-CHOKED BANGWEULU

A hundred and fifty miles south of Tanganyika lies Lake
Bangweulu. It occupies a depression in a tableland 3700 feet
above sea level. Sixty by 40 miles in extent, its area has been
computed at 1900 square miles, but its indefinite boundaries are
degenerating into mere marshland.

A fog of mystery obscured the lake in those days when
Africa was, indeed, the Dark Continent. Although its name,
variously spelled, was known to the Portuguese Dr. Lacerda
as far back as 1798, the first white man who is known to have
seen its lotus-scented waters was the missionary adventurer,
David Livingstone.

Bangweulu is an overflow of the headwaters of the Congo,
hugest of African rivers and, next to the Amazon, the greatest
river system on earth. It is a dying lake, rapidly approaching
extinction.

From the south the Luapula River enters the lake, a sluggish
stream nearly a mile wide, to form one of the many affluents
of the Congo. But the source of that vast river is probably the
Chambezi, which loses itself in the tangle of marshes stretching southwestward for forty miles or more. These were once
part of a greater Bangweulu which also embraced Lake Kam-
polombo, 20 miles long by 8 wide, not far from the Luapula
outlet.

Between them the two rivers are slowly obliterating Bangweulu, for the Chambezi is filling the marshes, while the Luapula drains the shoaling waters to convert them into swamps
and ultimately jungle. Nowhere does the depth exceed fifteen
feet.

The countryside teems with wild life, particularly hippos

and crocodiles, but the morose Cape buffalo is not so numerous as formerly.

Livingstone discovered Bangweulu in 1868. He noted this occurrence in his journal: "Walked a little way out and saw the shores of the lake for the first time, thankful that I had come safely thither."

He was so impressed by the region that he returned some years later, believing that here was the true source of the Nile. The fate that had befallen Dr. Lacerda might have deterred him, for that cultured Portuguese, having discovered the Chambezi, crossed it only to succumb to fever. Livingstone traversed Bangweulu in a canoe, pausing at Matipa Island, then plunged into the festering swamps, where he was stricken with dysentery. Faithful natives carried him to higher ground, built him a thatched hut, and when on May 1, 1873, he died while kneeling in prayer beside his lonely bunk, they buried his heart under a Mpundu, one of the most beautiful of African trees. The Royal Geographical Society has replaced that tree with a stone shaft surmounted by a cross. Although Livingstone was mistaken in his geography, and his last project left uncompleted, his good influence lived after him. Others carried on the work until that unknown area into which he had ventured at the cost of his life was thrown open to the world.

In the swamps of Bangweulu dwell the almost aquatic Batwa aborigines. Poulette Weatherley, who sojourned there in 1896, wrote some interesting memoirs. Respected by the natives as a just man and a dead shot, he carried with him a steel boat in sections, a welcome improvement over a dugout canoe. He was struck by the prosperity of the islands, with their gardens of cassava, sweet potatoes, bananas, and other fruits and vegetables, and flocks of goats and fat-tailed sheep. Hippos were trapped in pits. Although he suffered from insect bites, and his skin was poisoned by the euphorbia tree, he found the lake invested with an appealing charm. The marshes were often fringed with white sand beaches, while the tangled landscape of still waters and rank vegetation was particularly lovely when sunsets dyed the lagoons a rich crimson. Fish were plentiful and once he observed a python swim by, his head above the surface, then, diving, dart underwater with incredible swiftness. The natives told him the huge serpent was fishing.

Weatherley found the mouth of the Chambezi hidden in a vast sea of papyrus and was informed that in the dry season this great river was so reduced that the main channel barely floated a canoe. In the Luapula outlet he found only four feet of water, densely mantled with water lilies, white, lilac, and deep purple in color.

A mingled land- and waterscape, of fascinating vistas, was his description of Bangweulu.

CAVERNOUS LAKE NYASA

To most of us the Zambezi is only another river linked with picturesque characters like Trader Horn. Those who are more "up" in their geography, recall its plunge into a frightful earth crack nearly 400 feet deep at Victoria Falls, which rivals Niagara. But the Zambezi has other points of interest. It is one of Africa's four great rivers, the only one which empties into the Indian Ocean, and it drains one of the grandest bodies of fresh water in the world.

This is Nyasa. It lies some distance to the south and east of Tanganyika and three hundred and fifty miles from the sea. Crossed by the 14th parallel of south latitude, it is one of the most southerly of the world's great lakes. Only Titicaca and the playas of South America and Australia extend farther beyond the Equator.

Nyasa, still an international boundary, was once a focal

point of expanding empires. Its western shore is fringed by the
elongated British protectorate of Nyasaland; the northern juts
into Tanganyika Territory, formerly German East Africa,
while the remainder of the eastern coast borders Mozambique,
one of the few relics of the fabulous Portuguese dominions.

Nyasa's major axis extends almost north and south for 350
miles. Like Tanganyika, its maximum width is 45, while its
area is 11,000 square miles. This is sufficiently impressive, but
its volume is more so. Moore, in 1899, made his deepest sounding 2580 feet. As the lake surface lies at an altitude of 1650
feet, its bed is below sea level. As its depth is pretty uniform,
increasing with the abrupt declivity of the surrounding terrain,
it ranks in volume with Baikal, Tanganyika, and Superior
among the world's great reservoirs of fresh water. Neither so
deep nor so extensive as Tanganyika, some British investigators, nevertheless, believe that it contains even more water.

Nyasa is a product of the Great African Rift. The western
valley which embraces Tanganyika accounts for much of its
depth, but the more ancient and less well-defined mid rift and
eastern rift also converge upon its shores. Deep as it is, lacustrine beaches notch the surrounding heights 700 feet above
present levels.

Northwestward, clear to Tanganyika, stretches a lofty
tableland not unfavorable to Europeans. Around the northern
shores curve the Livingstone Mountains, with peaks 10,000
feet above the bottom of the Nyasa trough. Here the country
is particularly varied and attractive. The northwestern coast
line is dominated by the sandstone heights of Mount Waller,
while about the southern sector cluster the Mapangi Hills,
3000 feet high. Here the lake becomes restricted between
rocky promontories. The eastern shore is broken by alluvial
belts and marshy stretches. On the whole, the coast line is
regular, the islands few in number and of no great size.

The Portuguese had some notion of Nyasa, but there is no

record that they ever traversed the difficult country which separates it from the sea. It also lay beyond the sphere of Arab ivory seekers and slave traders, familiar with both Tanganyika and Victoria. In 1859 David Livingstone first sighted the big lake at about the same time that the German, Albrecht Roscher, reached it from another direction. In 1876 the northern shores were surveyed by Edward Young, while maps of increasing accuracy have since been plotted.

Visitors never fail to comment upon the beauty of Nyasa and its countryside. Sir Alfred Sharpe was impressed with its deep blue color in contrast with Tanganyika's green, and found its waters delightfully sweet and refreshing. Small flies known as nkungu rise in dense swarms from the shallows. Far from considering these an annoyance, however, the natives capture them in basketlike nets, roll them into a ball between the palms of the hands, and pronounce them delicious.

Nyasa is believed to be of more recent origin than Tanganyika. Sir Alfred Sharpe thought he could detect appreciable tides of five or six inches. The surface shows seasonal variations from the influx of streams descending the lofty tableland, while even more interesting are cyclical changes following a yet undetermined period of years.

These cycles have been studied in the capricious action of the Shiré River outlet at the southern tip. Some miles distant, on its way to join the Zambezi, this river broadens into another lake, Pamalombe, roughly circular and 15 miles across. Farther to the south and east, but in the same Riftian valley, is a still larger lake called Shirwa or Chilwa, 40 miles long by 15 broad. Presumably both lakes were once embraced in a greater Nyasa.

In 1925 the Shiré became so impeded with shoals that flat-bottomed steamers could no longer descend it to the sea, while Pamalombe was reported entirely dried up. Three years later, however, the lake level had risen, while in 1940 it was reported at its known maximum.

Engineering skill may someday cope with such interruptions, for a commercial waterway from the ocean to this rich hinterland is too inviting to be ignored.

Not only trading steamers but British gunboats have been introduced into Nyasa, while in the days of Kaiser Wilhelm the Germans also maintained their armed patrols. In World War I the forested heights re-echoed to gunfire as two great powers strove, even in this remote region, for world dominance. Such warfare is now ended, and territory so rich in natural charm and proven resources should be suffered to develop in peace.

RUDOLF, A VAST SODA WATER

In that little frequented region where the Abyssinian highlands merge with the great equatorial plateau lies Lake Rudolf. Somewhat north of the eastern Rift, it is in the path of the main fracture which may be traced by other lakes trailing off in a northeasterly direction toward the Red Sea.

Rudolf is about two hundred and fifty miles northeast of Victoria Nyanza, mostly within the British province of Kenya, although its northern edge gouges into Abyssinia.

The surrounding terrain has undergone extraordinary upheavals. L. S. Leakey has outlined the bed of a huge fossil lake, extending hundreds of miles southward, which he called Kamasia. Around its shores he unearthed the bones of animals now extinct, mingled with human bones which seemed to challenge comparison with the most venerable of such relics anywhere. Stone instruments included specimens of an advanced hand ax culture. A far heavier rainfall must have prevailed at that time.

In this ancient basin, shut off from the sea, scattered remnants of the Kamasian lake survive. Of these the largest is Rudolf. One hundred and eighty-five miles in length by 37 broad, its area, 3475 square miles, places it number twenty-one among the big lakes of the world.

The surrounding country is generally sterile and forbidding. Most of the streams which meander lakeward are smothered in the sands. The one dependable tributary, the Omo, descends from the Abyssinian highlands to empty through a fine channel a quarter mile in width. Here lake waters are palatable, though elsewhere highly alkaline.

Rudolf has an elevation of 1250 feet. Volcanic cones loom all about. Near the northern end Mount Lubur, with a well-defined crater, towers nearly a mile. The southwestern corner is dominated by another volcano, Kulal, 7812 feet in height. C. F. Archer, who spent some time in the vicinity, found it split by a vast chasm 3000 feet deep and only 100 feet wide at the top! Farther south the loftier Mount Sil rears 9280 feet.

Of more immediate interest is Mount Teleki, also in the southern sector. This volcano was named for its discoverer, Count Teleki, who found it in violent eruption, a five-mile lava flow compelling a wide detour. Some years later English investigators failed to locate the cone, which natives reported had blown up in a violent paroxysm. A. L. Champion, however, rediscovered Teleki, then about a thousand feet above lake levels, quiescent but menacing with jets of steam.

Around Rudolf's southern shore steep cliffs disclose the Rift fracture for more than a hundred miles. The western shores open upon arid plains of sparse vegetation dominated by hills reaching a height of 3470 feet. Farther north the Hummurr range culminates in peaks above 7000 feet.

The eastern coast is lower and in places marshy. Sand spits, extending into the lake as much as five miles, enclose almost isolated lagoons. Aside from such irregularities, the outline is fairly uniform, save in the northwest, where Sanderson's Gulf, thirty-five miles long, is nearly landlocked by two projecting points.

Although vague rumors about the big lake had long since reached the seacoast, the first European visitors of record were the Hungarian Count Samuel Teleki and his companion, Lieutenant Ludwig von Hohnel. Leaving Zanzibar in 1886 with a retinue of five hundred natives, they returned three years later with only two hundred. Approaching the lake in 1888 through a thirsty land, they found its water anything but palatable, so heavy was the soda content. Natives in the vicinity drink it, but Europeans first treat it with citric acid. Teleki named the lake for a member of the Austrian imperial family, a variation in the regal nomenclature, mainly British, of other African lakes.

Not only is the surrounding country studded with volcanoes, but the three principal islands show extinct cones. Known as North, Central and South islands, they rear up from the lake bed, each in its own sector.

North Island is mountainous, rising 2100 feet above the lake. Central Island, though lower, is more striking, for its scant two square miles of area encloses three distinct crater lakes. Pitted with fumaroles emitting sulphur fumes, they are surrounded by sheer cliffs 550 feet high. Their waters, greener than Rudolf's and more alkaline, swarm with crocodiles. The South Island, or Elmolo, ten miles long, is much the largest. Its inhabitants navigate makeshift rafts and use fish spears of oryx horn! West of Rudolf a degenerate tribe called Teuth subsist upon roots, grubs, and small mammals.

Reports of fluctuating lake levels are conflicting. James Harrison, who led an expedition from Abyssinia in 1899, was certain that this level had fallen many feet within a few years. He passed through villages filled with corpses, gruesome mementos of a season of drought. Approaching the lake, however, he entered a country swarming with elephants, rhinos, buffalo, giraffes, and lions. Here he narrowly escaped death from a charging cow elephant.

About the same time Major Austin, exploring the south-eastern coast, found the lake waters rising, as he observed palm trees in the shallows three miles offshore. He noted many hippos and crocodiles, while the lagoons swarmed with fla-mingos, ibises, spoonbills, pelicans, and herons by the million. The waters were so charged with soda that they barely quenched the thirst. Amid outlying hills a number of streams were swallowed up in the sands.

Along the sandy spits of this coast, huge lake turtles and fish of various species abound. E. B. Worthington caught a Nile perch more than six feet long which tipped the scales at 214 pounds. For however barren the neighboring country, Rudolf's bitter waters fairly teem with life.

CHAD IN LEGEND AND REALITY

From travelers' tales, fragmentary and highly colored, Ptolemy seems to have gained some inkling of a great lake beyond the Sahara. Although far to the west, it was portrayed upon ancient maps as one of the sources of the Nile. Similar rumors in more recent times have fomented political intrigue and rivalry.

This much-discussed body of inland waters is Lake Chad. While Africa's other big lakes are grouped in an area about 1500 miles long by 600 broad, much nearer the Indian Ocean than the Atlantic, Chad is on the opposite side of the continent. Fourteen hundred miles of difficult terrain separate it from Albert Nyanza, nearest of those big lakes. The Libyan Gulf, closest approach of the Mediterranean, is twelve hundred miles distant, the Gulf of Guinea, that vast indentation of western

Africa, seven hundred. Of all great lakes, Chad was long the most remote and inaccessible.

What little was known to a civilization confined within the Mediterranean area filtered across the greatest desert in the world. But that desert is not the sandy waste of popular fancy. On the contrary, of its more than 3,500,000 square miles, roughly equal to all Europe, scarcely a fifth is sand. The characteristic landscape is a series of rocky plateaus broken by the beds of dried-up rivers and dead lakes. Mountain regions culminate in peaks over 11,000 feet high, and vast areas produce a sparse vegetation sufficient to support starveling goats and camels. Certain species of antelopes that have never been known to drink roam even its most sterile barrens, while occasional oases break the drab monotony.

At least two million people call the Sahara home. The camel is their means of transportation, its milk their favorite beverage. Camels, dates, and salt are the chief commodities of commerce.

Across this inhospitable region for thousands of years a trade route has led from Morocco to Timbuktu, that city invested with the charm of the Arabian Nights in the valley of the great Niger River. There, where "canoe and camel meet," tales of regions to the eastward were long current.

Out of such nebulous gossip Chad assumed tangible form. It is a dying lake, slowly succumbing to an implacable climate, aided by the encroachment of the desert. Like Rudolf, it has no outlet to the sea. Although it lies on the edge of the equatorial rain belt, a few degrees north of the Equator, the northern portion of its basin has dried up, leaving Chad an exposed bastion projecting into the barrens. In the struggle between lake and desert the melancholy conclusion seems inevitable.

To the north and east sandy hills mark the advance skirmish line of the Sahara. Here lake shallows seem to be literally shriveling up. On a chain of islands stretching from five to twenty miles from shore, a native tribe called Buduma live in thatched huts with their herds of cattle. They keep in touch with the outer world by boats of rushes resembling rude gondolas. On one island a band of ferocious pirates was subdued by the French. These islands, formed of clay from the lake bed mingled with wind-blown sand, are gradually merging with the mainland, while new islands appear in the offing. The many lagoons, scarcely three feet deep, purify the waters as the salt in the solution is deposited there, so that the lake itself remains fresh, becoming slightly brackish only in periods of drought. In 1905 Lieutenant Audoin of the French Army, exploring these lagoons, found a maze of channels in which an explorer might become hopelessly involved, to perish among muddy sloughs.

Even in the middle of the lake the depth rarely exceeds twenty feet. In places mud flats appear, elsewhere dense growths of vegetation. Through aquatic jungles of papyrus and Nile cabbage flat boats are poled in water seldom more than six feet deep, while clouds of bloodsucking flies and mosquitoes add to the discomfort of the stifling heat.

Few lake contours are so indefinite as those of Chad, hence exact measurements are difficult if not impossible. Early in the century the English explorer, Boyd Alexander, who was later murdered near the Wadai-Darfur frontier, drew a sketch map. He found the lake divided by impassable swamps into a northern and southern sector. Even there natives frequently waded waist deep in soft mud to drag his boat across a thin film of water. Mrs. Patrick Ness, who visited the region in 1931, thought the lake dimensions might be 130 by 30 miles. More recent French maps show Alexander's bisecting obstruction as a vast peninsula, with clear water connecting north and south. And finally, aeronautical maps shed a more reliable light on what has so long remained a confused and confusing puzzle. They reveal the lake as sprawling over a vast area of rather

more than 10,000 square miles, 130 miles in length, widening
to 110 toward the south. Of this area a good third is broken
up into swamps, some labeled navigable, others impassable,
with perhaps an equal area listed as mud flats. The remaining
clear portions are studded with innumerable islands, while the
major outline is a tattered segment of mingled sand, swamp,
and water. In flood time the estimated lake area is 6500 square
miles.

Captain Tilho has traced the shore lines of a huge dead lake
which he estimates may once have rivaled the Caspian. Of this
inland sea, Chad remains only a tattered fragment.

The first European of record to reach its shores was Sir
Walter Oudney in 1823. Since 1850 the waters had evaporated
so rapidly that the turn of the century found dry land advancing everywhere in brigades of shoals and islands until the lake
was almost bisected by marshes. Even the northern and southern lobes were becoming greatly restricted. Northern waters
were clear, the southern yellowed with silt. Their shallowness
made them subject to violent agitation by the winds, but they
remained fresh and well stocked with fish.

Former tributaries have become dry wadis, so that the lake
is now sustained only by two considerable streams, one of
which has fallen under the baleful influence of the Sahara.
This is the Yobe, from well-watered Nigeria, which enters
the lake from the west but is robbed of much moisture by the
parching atmosphere. In 1921 F. W. Migeod, in the *Geographical Review*, reported no water whatever at its mouth,
although the bottom sands were moist. He observed trees
dying in dried-up swamps, formerly part of the lake itself,
while venerable natives had once seen hippos wallow in shallows now only salt pans.

A more dependable affluent is the Shari, approaching from
the south. In floodtime it inundates many a mud flat until
grateful boatmen find an extreme lake depth of 24 feet. But

unless the present trend is arrested, it seems doubtful whether such contributions can long withstand the parching winds from the desert. For the Shari also bears a burden of silt which gradually fills up the lake bed until shallows turn to swamps and swamps to millet fields.

Meanwhile, native villages, continually shifting their location, move southward as the tide of human life recedes from once fertile shores. That this retreat is not a rout, however, but an alternate ebb and flow is evidenced by a report in 1940 that lake levels had once more attained the elevation of 1903.

During the past century, when Chad was the theme of glowing commercial prospectuses, three world powers reached greedily for a segment of its coast line. The British, pushing northward from Nigeria, appropriated a broad sector on the south and west; the Germans established a "bridgehead" by driving a narrow wedge from their possessions in Kamerun, while the French, sweeping southward across the Sahara, assumed control over the remainder.

But these exploiters of Africa were doomed to disappointment. The shallow waters offered no possibilities as a trade route. The Germans were eliminated in World War I, and now both French and British seem waiting apathetically for the once great lake to die. If the Shari should alter its course, Chad, with all its traditions, would soon join those other nameless lakes long since engulfed by the insatiable Sahara.

THE GREAT MAKARIKARI PLAYA

In the southern half of Africa, midway between the Indian and Atlantic Oceans, is a singular region little known to the outer world. On some maps it appears as the Makarikari Lake, on others as a swamp. It is neither, but rather a vast playa or salar, one of those intermittent lakes that hover on the brink of extinction.

Some seven hundred miles southwest of Nyasa and a good thousand north and east of the Cape of Good Hope, it is confined within the British protectorate of Bechuanaland. Here the Kalahari Desert has insured that dismal fate with which the Sahara threatens Lake Chad. For the Makarikari is little better than the ghost of a dead lake which once moistened a parching atmosphere.

It lies in the heart of a vast interior drainage basin. Whether this ever had an outlet to the sea is uncertain. The Botletle River, approaching from the north, is the principal affluent, but most of its dwindling current evaporates. On the east the smaller Nata River suffers the same fate. Elsewhere dry ravines mark former watercourses.

Exact measurements of the Makarikari are unavailable. Captain Clifford, who went there in a lorry in 1928, thought it might be 160 miles long by 60 wide. He crossed several dried-up bays and even ventured toward the center but his lorry broke through the saline crust and was extricated with difficulty. Upon his sketch map the lake bed appears as a parallelogram with wavy edges suggesting a flag fluttering in the breeze.

The captain, now Sir Bede Clifford, made his third examination in 1939. Approaching from the north, he followed a tonguelike peninsula to its tip, then drove straight across the hard crust which glistened in the sun. An island emerged midway to the southern shore, but no water was visible anywhere. This time his more accurate sketch map revised former dimensions downward to a more moderate 90 by 60 miles.

Even this estimate would rank the Makarikari among the world's big lakes, had not its contents so nearly disappeared. A few pools of brine accumulate in seasons when the scant rainfall is more abundant than usual, while native cattle have become accustomed to the brackish water of the neighborhood.

The aborigines who frequent the arid hinterland to the south are few in number and nomads by necessity. Most of them are bushmen who once ranged all the way to the cape. Sir Bede found their keen sense of direction an animal instinct, as they seldom glanced at the sun and never traveled at night when the stars might prove useful guides, as they are in the Arabian desert.

Professor E. H. L. Schwartz has advocated refilling the Makarikari by diverting several African rivers, only to encounter the usual criticism and opposition. Whatever its merits, such a project belongs to a more enlightened future when man learns, by conserving a dwindling water supply, to control his climate.

MINOR AFRICAN LAKES

1. TANA

In addition to its inland seas of fresh, saline, or brackish water, Africa has a number of lesser lakes which deserve mention.

We have observed how the main branch of the Nile drains such imposing bodies of water as Victoria and Albert Nyanza. The shorter or so-called Blue Nile has its principal reservoir in sapphire-tinted Tana.

This beautiful lake nestles in the lofty tableland of Abyssinia, more than a mile above sea level, at an altitude of 5690 feet. Roughly heart-shaped, its greatest length 47, its maximum width 44 miles, it covers an area of 1100 square miles in a drainage basin of 5400. The annual rainfall of 39 inches maintains the lake level by three considerable streams and several lesser ones. Many rocky promontories define the shores, while the surrounding peaks, the loftiest 15,200 feet in height, make the scenery wild, varied, and attractive.

The lake was formerly called Dembea, but it was known to Ptolemy as Coloe Palus and placed upon his map of Africa. From it issued the Astapos River—the modern Abbai. This stream enters the southeastern sector, flows through the lake with a perceptible current, and emerges at the southwestern corner. Both the ancient Astapos and the modern Abbai are other names for the Blue Nile.

Toward the lake's southern extremity is a rocky group 8 miles long by 4 wide known as the Dek Islands. Of basaltic origin, precipitous and green with verdure, they have a savage loveliness. Henry Blanc, who led an expedition into the region after obtaining permission from that surly despot, the Emperor Theodore, found the view from these islands more beautiful than Geneva.

Though doubtless visited by Greek and Egyptian traders, Tana was rediscovered in 1625 by the Portuguese priest, Father Lobo.

The countryside is nominally independent under Abyssinian rule. But Great Britain has long had an economic interest in the lake as an important source of those waters, impounded by the Assouan Dam, which help to irrigate Egypt's farmlands.

2. MWERU

A lesser member of the great Congo system is Lake Mweru. A hundred miles west of Tanganyika and somewhat to the southward, it occupies a portion of the African Rift at an elevation of 3000 feet.

Roughly rectangular, Mweru is 68 miles long by 25 broad. It seems to have been discovered by Dr. Lacerda in 1798, shortly before he was stricken by a fatal fever. Livingstone visited the lake in 1867, noting the abundance of wild game, while it was first circumnavigated by Sir Alfred Sharpe in 1890.

Near its southern extremity it receives the Luapula, bearing the overflow from Bangweulu. Traversing the long axis of the lake, this stream emerges as the Lualaba, one of the many branches of the Congo.

The shore line of Mweru is low, obscured in places by mangrove swamps, and described as "uninteresting." A considerable island lies in the southern sector. In 1900 a small steamer was borne to the lake in sections to be there reassembled.

Mweru is another boundary lake, between the Belgian Congo and Northern Rhodesia. Lying within the sphere of influence of two European powers, it may yet become the nucleus of a considerable commerce when the surrounding terrain, rich in undeveloped resources, is more fully exploited.

3. RUKWA

A pathetic relic of former greatness is Lake Rukwa. Speke, exploring Tanganyika, heard of it as an impassable swamp, but Joseph Thompson seems to have been the first European to view its erratic waters. In 1880, from a height of 8000 feet, he beheld it far below, surrounded by rugged terrain, seemingly so near that he said, "I could almost throw a stone into it."

Rukwa, which is about midway between Tanganyika and Nyasa, occupies the lower portion of the Nyasa trough in the tremendous African Rift. There is no outlet. Beaches all about mark the borders of a much larger lake that must have been at least three hundred feet deeper. Some of this ancient bed has become a grassy flat which overflows in time of rainfall. The lake waters, brackish rather than saline, are so shallow that an increased depth of ten or fifteen feet profoundly affects their area. In 1929 the lake had shrunk to a length of 30 miles, while ten years later it had expanded to 80 with a width of 25. It then approached the dimensions of the world's lesser big lakes.

Such fluctuations are caused by the varying influx of streams pouring down from the heights. Like the last convulsive spasms of the dying individual, they mark the beginning of the end.

4. THE SODA LAKES

A hundred and fifty miles seaward from the southern shores of Victoria Nyanza lie the so-called Soda Lakes. They occupy the lowest levels of a vast depression where the earth crust, blocked out by fractures, has fallen in. The smaller, called Magadi, was visited by Captain E. G. Smith in 1904. He found the outline most irregular, traversed by great ridges and flanked by mile-wide strips that had sunken like gigantic furrows. The lake was about 20 miles long by 5 or more in width, yet the water seemed only a few inches deep. He observed several streams both cold and hot, the latter heavily impregnated with soda, flowing into the lake, while all about springs of soda water gushed up through the caked crust. This dyed the waters a vivid pink, a color heightened by thousands of rosy flamingos that waded about, thrusting their crooked beaks into the mud. Meanwhile, the Englishman observed that the water cracked his boots and inflamed his porters' bare feet.

A railway from the shores of the Indian Ocean now leads to Magadi, where a British company is salvaging some of its fabulous deposits of salt and gypsum.

South of Magadi, in what was once German Tanganyika, lies still larger Lake Natron. The name is suggestive, for according to Webster, Natron is native sodium carbonate, akin to that powdery drug so popular for indigestion. This lake is about 40 miles long by 20 broad. All about tower lofty peaks, several over nine thousand feet high, while Elanairobi is 10,528. In 1940 Oldonyo L'Enghai—the Mountain of God—near the southern shore, erupted violently. The region is one of confused volcanic disturbances, and the waters heavily charged with mineral.

John Parkinson, who visited Natron in 1912, left a vivid word picture. So uncanny was the landscape that it seemed to belong more properly to another world. From a neighboring height he gazed out over a vast bowllike depression with walls of purple lava, enclosing a broad expanse of white alkaline shallows. As if to embellish the color scheme, brown mud flats appeared here and there, encrusted with pink patches, while beyond their gaudy surface volcanic cones deluged the sky with inky-black smoke.

V

Asian Lakes

THE PEERLESS CASPIAN

The grandest body of inland water in the world is the Caspian. Extending 795 miles from north to south by 275 wide, its area, including islands, is 169,300 square miles.

More than five times as large as Superior, its dimensions are so vast that it is seldom considered a lake at all, yet it conforms to all the details of the definition. Even Marco Polo recognized this when he called it the "Sea of Abaku" which "partakes of the nature of a lake not communicating with any sea."

Nor is the Caspian less entitled to be called a Sea. Not only would its waters fill the combined North and Baltic seas to overflowing, but it is a remnant of the Eurasian Mediterranean or Sarmatian Sea which once overspread a wider area connecting with the Sea of Azov. Before the dawn of Pliocene times, however, the emergence of broad plateaus and lofty mountain ranges had broken up this immense sheet of water into the Caspian, the Aral Sea, and numerous lesser lakes which now dot the landscape. During the last glacial period, the Caspian seems to have overflowed into the Black Sea, but its subsiding waters now lie 86 feet below sea level, and great stretches of the Russian plains to the north are also involved in this depression.

The Caspian's oceanic origin may be traced both in neighboring beaches and in the persistence of many forms of marine life. Seals still furnish an important industry in Krasnovodsk Bay, while among other species more at home in the ocean are

salmon, herring, and lobsters, together with many mollusks, sponges, and worms. Some resemble Arctic types, hinting at a former communication with that icy sea, while not a few, become highly specialized, are found nowhere else.

The Caspian is an impressive example of a lake recaptured from the sea. To be sure, it has not lost its salinity, like Onega or Nicaragua, but when we consider that it occupies one of those isolated drainage basins which are natural receptacles for mineral matter, its comparative freshness is remarkable.

Over its extensive area saline content varies greatly. Along the northern shores the waters are little more than brackish, while in that curious gulf known as Kara Bugaz they are supersaturated with minerals.

F. W. Clarke, in his study of lake waters, places the Caspian in the fourth of his nine divisions, as sulphato chloride, because of the sulphates it contains. The average "saltness" is difficult to determine, and investigators disagree. Most authorities give this content as about three eighths that of the ocean, but a recent tabulation lists it at 6.29 grams per liter in contrast with the Atlantic's 35.06, or less than one fifth. Like the Black Sea, the Caspian becomes stagnant below the 220-fathom mark, where oxygen yields to poisonous hydrogen sulphide.

The Caspian lies in a drainage basin more than three quarters as extensive as the entire Mississippi Valley. Europe's biggest river, the Volga, contributes the accumulated waters of 560,-000 square miles. Other affluents are the shallow Ural, once considered part of the boundary between Europe and Asia, the impetuous Terek, swollen with the snows of the Caucasus, and many lesser streams. The influx of fresh water has been estimated at 175 cubic miles annually, sufficient to create a lake larger than Erie, or to raise the level of the Caspian some five and a half feet.

This enormous volume, however, barely offsets evaporation, intensified by parching winds from Asia. The surface level, that fluctuates with the seasons and still more through longer cycles, shows a downward tendency. At the beginning of the fourteenth century it was more than forty feet higher than at present, while Soviet scientists have reported a decline of six and a half feet during the past ten years. In that brief period they estimate that 31,000,000,000,000 gallons had evaporated —four times the volume of the Sea of Azov!

Inflowing rivers and prevalent winds create movements which parallel ocean currents. There is a steady creeping of the waters down the western shore, an upward drift along the eastern coast. Barometric disturbances, accompanied by gales, sometimes pile up the waters on exposed beaches eight feet above normal levels.

The Caspian is so huge that it is best examined by dividing it into three sections to conform with the surrounding terrain. Into the northern section flows the Ural River, much impeded by shoals. To the eastward the sea sweeps in a broad semicircle, its shores marked by low calcareous hills, broken by the Gulf of Kaidak, which penetrates inland like a vermiform appendix. According to recent reports, this gulf is now drying up. West of the Ural the Volga pours majestically through a broad delta which so encroaches upon the lake that steamers wishing to enter this great artery of commerce must lighten their cargoes when forty miles offshore. This sector is being so rapidly silted up that the depth rarely exceeds a hundred and twenty feet. Southward from the mouth of this great river the coast line, for a hundred and seventy miles, is gashed by thousands of narrow bays or lagoons called limans, some of them thirty miles long and separated by low hills or sand dunes. They fringe the mainland like the edge of a tattered fabric.

The midsection of the Caspian is somewhat restricted between the arid Ust-Urt plateau on the east and the hoary summits of the Caucasus on the west, dominated by Mount

Elbruz, loftiest of European peaks, 18,471 feet high. To the north of this range the Terek River irrupts through a barricade of islands that it pushes continuously outward into deeper water. The region is rich in legend. Upon the granite flanks of Caucasus, the gods of ancient Greece chained Prometheus for his theft of fire from heaven. Even now discordant races mingle in an ethnic whirlpool of languages and customs. Near Derbent, in Daghestan, the mountains approach the sea, leaving a narrow ribbon of terrain called the Albanae Portae or the Caspiae Pylae. Here Marco Polo reminds us, "Alexander the Great—unable to penetrate because of the narrowness and difficulty of a certain pass—on one side washed by the sea and confined on the other by high mountains and woods—caused a great wall to be built. . . . From its uncommon strength the pass was called the Gate of Iron."

Some distance to the south the peninsula of Apsheron juts out into the lake—a rocky spur more than forty miles long. On its southern lea nestles the great port of the Caspian, Baku, with a wartime population of 810,000.

On the opposite or eastern side of the sea, which here attains a depth of half a mile, the Ust-Urt plateau is invaded by that singular pouch of waters called the Kara Bugaz. This landlocked gulf, embracing 7100 square miles, is almost isolated by two elongated sandy points which nearly come together. Through the intervening channel, in places little more than a hundred meters wide and over a mile long, a steady torrent from the Caspian, flowing from one and a half to five miles per hour, pours 22,000 cubic feet of water a second, which never returns. Spreading out over an area nearly as large as Lake Ontario, this water, bluish yellow in color, often scarcely three feet deep and never more than forty, evaporates in the hot sun. When chilled in winter, it precipitates some of its mineral solution as sulphate of magnesia, which covers 1300 square miles of the shallow bottom to an extreme

depth of seven feet, an estimated total of 1,000,000,000 tons!
No wonder the Kara Bugaz has been termed a gigantic natural
crucible for the production of Epsom salts! The withdrawal
of so much mineral matter has doubtless aided in freshening
the entire Caspian content. South of this enormous drying pan
the Balkhan Mountains raise their rugged peaks to a height of
more than a mile.

The third or southern sector of the Caspian is much the
deepest, for here the sounding line has run out 3612 feet, into
lacustrine abysses unrivaled elsewhere save in Tanganyika
and Baikal. Soviet territory grips it between the so-called
Republic of Turkomen on the east and Georgia on the west,
but southward its shores form a broad indentation in the outline of Iran or ancient Persia. Here the Caspian approaches
the Elburz Mountains topped by 18,600-foot Demavend, even
higher than the Caucasus. Hundreds of streams race across a
coastal strip varying from twenty to forty miles in width,
which has been termed a "swamp in winter, a hothouse in
summer." Although cursed by malaria, it is wonderfully fertile, producing cotton, tobacco, semitropical fruits, and mul-
berries, the basis of a considerable silk industry. Here, also,
are fields aflame with opium poppies, suggesting that sensuous
atmosphere which pervades the verses of Omar Khayyám.

From prehistoric times the Caspian has served as an effective
barrier against invasion and a broad highway of commerce.
Human tides from Asia have either veered northward through
the flat lands of Russia into Central Europe or southward
through Persia into the Near East. The Romans, in their era
of greatest expansion, reached its western shores when armies
bearing the standards of aggressive Chinese emperors were
approaching from the east. It remains one of the intriguing
speculations of history: what might have happened had those
two dissimilar cultures mingled at that time? But then, as now,
the Caspian was an almost impassable obstruction.

Commercial activities are hampered in the northern area by the severe Russian·winter. The Volga is icebound for an average of 112 days out of the year, while the upper reaches of the Ural are even more restricted. Here, also, the surface of the Caspian is frozen around the seacoast, where grain ships from Russia meet petroleum tankers from the Caucasus in enforced idleness.

Marco Polo noted that Genoese merchants had "begun to navigate it [the Caspian] and they bring from thence the kind of silk called Ghellie." He also mentioned another commodity destined to become far more important: "a fountain of oil —good for camels that have the mange—also good for burning. In the neighboring country no other is used in their lamps and people come from distant parts to obtain it."

From this description we catch our first glimpse of the great oil wells near Baku which supply Russia with most of its petroleum. The original fountains still trickle with liquid black gold, while all about a forest of steel derricks surmounts drilled wells. To Baku come many tankers and freight ships bearing assorted merchandise. In this ancient city, long held by the Persians, the Mohammedan mosque and palace of the khan are still preserved. In its busy marts East and West meet to exchange commodities which range from oriental embroideries and carpets to modern machinery.

Petroleum is not the only mineral wealth of the Caspian basin. The salt hills of southern Russia were known in medieval times. In the fastnesses of the Caucasus are found ores of copper, molybdenum, and other metals, together with the largest known deposits of manganese, that indispensable alloy of certain types of steel.

Long famed for its fisheries, the Caspian nets and seines a fortune annually from its salmon, herring, and lesser species. The patriarch of the clan is the huge sturgeon, which sometimes attains a length of twenty feet and a weight of three thousand pounds. From the swimming bladder isinglass is manufactured, while the eggs or roe, under the name of caviar, are a familiar product of the region.

The Caspian was dimly known to the ancients. Strabo thought its name was derived from the Caspii, a barbaric tribe which inhabited its remoter shores. Maps of the period sometimes had it opening into the polar ocean. Alexander the Great sent his admiral Parmenides to learn the facts, but when he died at Babylon, dreaming of a world still unconquered, Parmenides, confining his investigations to the southern sector, left the question unanswered. Aristotle, however, pictured it as a lake, as did Ptolemy on his maps.

The Mohammedan geographer, Al-Masudi, in the ninth century, listed the Caspian, which he called Khazan, as one of the seven seas into which the oceans were traditionally divided.

A focus of trade routes and pillaging armies from immemorial times, the Caspian looms once more as a storm center upon the troubled horizon. The Soviet Union, controlling most of its coastal terrain, covets the shore line of Iran, weakly held and incapable of self-defense. Let the circuit be completed, and this hugest of lakes, with its incalculable resources, will become a private ocean in the Red Empire.

THE ARAL SEA

In a lonely region of eastern Asia lies a body of water that has been enveloped for centuries in a fog of misunderstanding and uncertainty. The nomadic Kirghiz who sometimes visit its well-nigh deserted shores call it Aral-denghiz, the Sea of Islands, for it has many, but to the outside world it is the Aral Sea.

It was once a part of the far greater Sarmatian sea, of which the Caspian is a more conspicuous relic. Beaches are carved on the surrounding terrain, while shells of marine mollusks are unearthed in areas two hundred feet above present lake levels and at great distances. A chain of lakes through the Ust-Urt plateau leads to the Caspian, little more than two hundred miles to the west. The two were joined in the glacial period, although the Aral is now elevated 242 feet above its subsiding associate. In more remote times it extended northward to the Sea of Azov and the Black Sea, while rumors from a vague but still historic antiquity hint at an overflow across the low northern steppes to the headwaters of the Ob River and the Arctic. Such outlets, if they existed, have been closed by rising earth strata to confine the Aral to an independent drainage system.

The big lake is bisected by the 45th parallel of north latitude, fixing its position midway between the Equator and the Pole. Geographically, it is enclosed between the so-called Republic of Kazak and the adjoining Kara-Kalpak Republic on the south, in the Soviet Empire.

The surrounding country is singularly unattractive. Northward the empty steppes blend into the marshes of the Ob. Westward stretches the Ust-Urt plateau with its shifting dunes, its salt pans, and beds of bleaching gypsum, while to the east and southeast lies the Red Sand Desert. Only toward the south do more pleasing horizons open on the alluvial district of Khiva, with its flowers, its apricots, and melons "sweet as honey."

Though much reduced, the Aral, known as the Great Blue Sea of western Asia, is probably the third largest lake in the world as revised figures give it an area of 26,233 square miles, slightly more extensive than Victoria Nyanza. Its length is 280 miles, its width 130. Elevated 155 feet above sea level, its maximum depth is 222 feet, although the average probably does not exceed fifty.

Like the Caspian, its waters have freshened appreciably. According to recent reports, they show a salinity of 10.7 grams per liter or little more than two sevenths that of the Atlantic. Many of the abundant fish are fresh-water species.

Climate as well as topography have profoundly influenced the Aral. Fierce winds sweeping down from the steppes blow for months on end, fretting the shallows into a violence impassable for small boats. Hungry winds, greedy for moisture, with an average July temperature of well over 80 degrees, they would devour the entire lake were it not for the influx of two great rivers fed by the snows of distant mountain ranges.

One of these rivers, the Jaxartes or Syr Darya, enters the northeastern corner, sweeping downward from the Tien Shan —known to the Chinese as the Mountains of Heaven. The other, the Oxus or Amu Darya, enters the southern sector from the far-off watershed of the Hindu Kush. Although its surplus is diverted into Khiva's irrigation ditches, these two rivers, according to Major Herbert Wood, discharge into the Aral a minimum of 2000 cubic feet of water every second. Without this influx, the major affirms, the lake would disappear in half a century.

There is evidence that it has undergone profound fluctuations during recorded time. On ancient maps it projected a hundred miles farther south. In the Middle Ages rumor had it that the Aral had disappeared, a plausible exaggeration when we recall that as recently as 1880 travelers reported that it was rapidly drying up. On the other hand, the Russian expedition of 1900 found the waters, which were remarkably clear, expanding, while another expedition in 1910 thought the surface had risen nine feet!

One of the most curious factors in such instability is the fickle behavior of the Oxus. Prior to the fourteenth century a branch of that river seems to have gone wandering westward to empty into the Caspian. The noted English traveler, Anthony Jenkinson, in his journey to Turkestan in 1559, sailed across that sea from Russia, then up the Oxus, which he described as "greate and very swifte." He also mentioned a branch which flowed north instead of west, to disappear underground and reappear in a lake in China! That lake was presumably the Aral, for at various times Turkestan has acknowledged the overlordship of Cathay. The dry stream bed to the Caspian is still a theme of argument with geologists. In any case, the river now flows northward.

Maps scarcely a century old show it entering the Aral through a gulf 80 miles long by 20 broad. That gulf has become a swamp, fringed with millet fields. The delta of the Jaxartes has also increased by thirty-four square kilometers during the past fifty years. Although they sustain the Aral, these two great rivers are hastening its destruction by silt deposits in its broad but shallow basin.

The ancient Persian Empire embraced the southern shore of the Aral, then known as the Kwarizm. Alexander the Great gazed out over its troubled surface to speculate, no doubt, upon what unknown lands might lie beyond. Fishing boats now engage in their hazardous calling, their catches salted and exported to considerable distances. In line with the Soviet program for developing the vast Asian hinterland, two important ports have been established upon the Aral Sea, Kant Usyak on the south and Aralskoe More on the north, where camel caravans connect with a railroad across Turkestan. Government steamers also ship wheat from the great Siberian grain belt to southern markets. But there are few natural harbors and the littoral region remains largely uninhabited.

Not many lakes have had a more disturbed history than this forlorn ocean remnant in the continent of Asia, withered by parching winds and wholly dependent upon capricious rivers.

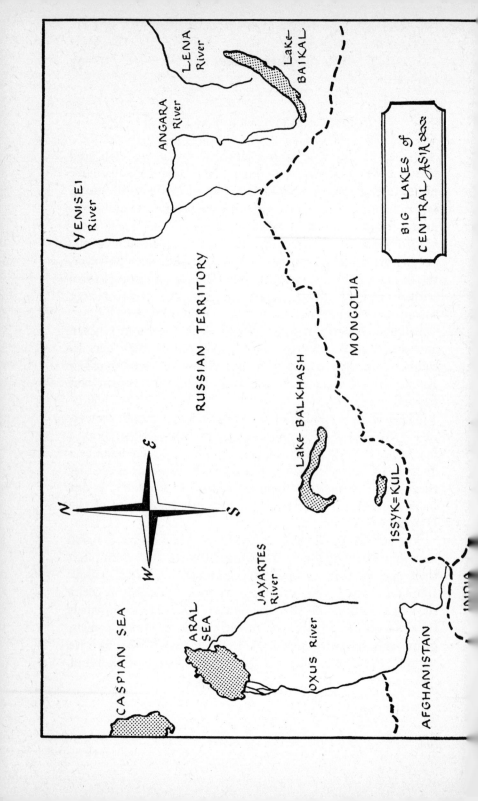

ELONGATED LAKE BALKHASH

A glance at the same large-scale map reveals an elongated body of water shaped something like a summer squash, or rather one of those slim gourds displayed in vegetable stores. It is called Lake Balkhash. Its curving convolutions may be followed roughly east and west for nearly 430 miles, a length exceeded only by Tanganyika and the Caspian among the world's great lakes. From tip to tip in a straight line, however, the distance is little more than 300, while its attenuated form with a maximum bulge of only 53 gives it an area of 7115 square miles, somewhat smaller than Lake Ontario.

Balkhash lies in the same latitude as the northern Caspian and the Aral Sea, for the 45th parallel of latitude cuts its southern tip. It is enclosed in that extensive territory called Kazak, which extends all the way from the Caspian and beyond.

The Kazaks, a branch of the Kirghiz racial group, are evidently of Tartar or Mongolian origin, though they speak a language of Turkish derivation. The name, which signifies a "horseman," reveals their customs, for the Russians assert that they were "born in the saddle." Kazak, incidentally, is our more familiar Cossack, although that matchless rider of the Don is of Slavic origin.

To the Kazak, Balkhash is known as Ala Tenghiz, a name more dignified and sonorous. Along its shores they often pitch their circular tents of black felt stretched over light willow frames, but they seldom remain very long. Not only is theirs the restlessness of inherent wanderlust, but necessity compels them to seek fresh pasturage for their flocks of horses, camels, goats, and fat-tailed sheep. A few, more settled, cultivate wheat, barley, and millet, the latter as the source of a kind of vodka. Their favorite drink, however, is kumiss, derived from fermented mare's milk; when feasting, they gorge themselves on mutton, goat's meat, and horseflesh. Nominally Sunnites, one of the "two and seventy jarring sects" of Islam that Omar Khayyám gently ridiculed, they retain their primitive beliefs in which their shamans placate Shaitan—the Evil One.

Garbed in flowing robes girdled at the waist, in wide-topped boots of black or red leather, and pointed hats of white felt, they make a picturesque appearance. The flute and the balalaika, a barbaric mandolin, invest their native songs with a wild and plaintive melody.

Suspicious of strangers, they are frank and straightforward in their dealings, like other untamed and perhaps untamable peoples. From just such reckless raiders Genghis Khan welded his invincible armies.

Needless to say, settled communities are infrequent along the extensive shore line, but at one place the Russians are engaged in developing some promising copper deposits.

Balkhash in many respects is unusual. Although extremely shallow, with a maximum depth of only 36 feet, and barred from all outlet to the sea, it has not degenerated into a salt lake. Brackish in some places, it has remained essentially fresh. At one time it was far more extensive. Its northern shores blend into those grim barrens known as the Famine Steppes; the southern, where sand and clay are interspersed with swamps, open upon more favorable terrain. There, among other vegetation, the kendyr plant grows wild; its tough fibers are useful for many purposes.

Several considerable rivers empty into the lake from the south or lose themselves in adjacent marshes. Most important is the Ili, which rises in the snowy Tien Shan. Others, including the Karatal and Lepsa, force their way through dense canebrakes or dissipate their currents in stagnant morasses, the haunt of Siberian tigers.

Surface levels fluctuate, like those of the Aral, not only seasonally, but over longer cycles. The average elevation above the ocean, however, remains about 900 feet. Winter locks Balkhash in icy fetters from November to April.

The fauna is restricted. Certain species of fish, particularly carp, are abundant, but the frog is unknown. While a former connection with the Aral Sea, six hundred miles to the westward, is improbable, there are stronger affinities with more remote and isolated drainage basins. Perhaps the untutored Kazaks are justified in feeling that the spirit of Shaitan broods over this elongated water of uncertain origin and peculiar characteristics.

ISSYK-KUL

Three hundred miles south of Balkhash, but separated by almost impassable mountains, lies Issyk-Kul. It fills the center of a depression in a lofty tableland more than a mile above the sea, for its elevation is given as 5400 feet. Even this is unimpressive compared with the two spurs of the mighty Tien Shan range which hem it in, the northern spur culminating in peaks more than 13,000 feet high, the southern topping 18,000. Yet through this valley migrating tribes have made a highway of the shores or across the treacherous surface of the lake.

Issyk-Kul, roughly lens-shaped, stretches east and west for 115 miles with a maximum breadth of 38. Its area is 2230 square miles or nearly that of the state of Delaware. It was long supposed to be shallow, but L. S. Berg, near the southern shore, sounded depths of over 2300 feet, suggesting a faulting of underlying strata.

Issyk-Kul was known to the Kalmucks as the Iron Lake, a picturesque description; but its name in the Kirghiz lan-

guage means Warm Lake, since it never freezes even in the
dead of winter, although ice fringes the shores. There are
evidences that the lake was once so much more voluminous
that it may have drained through one of the mountain
gorges toward the northwest. But within historic times the
waters were also considerably lower, as extensive ruins are
submerged.

Whatever its geological past, the lake is wholly isolated.
Hence, though fed by a number of mountain streams, it has
accumulated so much mineral matter that it is too brackish to
drink. An analysis of its saline content shows slightly over 3.5
parts of mineral per 1000, or about one tenth that of the
Atlantic.

The shores are sandy, with patches of clay broken by
marshes where lurk fierce old wild boars and still more formidable Siberian tigers. Here roving nomads of the On or right
branch of the Kara Kirghiz find winter pasturage for their
flocks.

Along the valley, in former times, Asiatic peoples have fled
westward from the ferocious Huns, who seem to have origi-
nated beyond the Great Wall of China and, sweeping across
two continents, ravaged the decrepit Roman Empire. Of these
enforced wanderers, the most interesting were the Uzans, who
found the valley so peaceful and sequestered that they loitered
there for two centuries or more. They seem to have disappeared about A.D. 500, perhaps absorbed by native tribes, perhaps venturing still farther westward—no one really knows.
But curious relics, including images of their forgotten stone
gods, are occasionally washed up by the lake.

Issyk-Kul has also been the cradle of other faiths. The
Chinese sage, Hsüan Tsang, left a vivid picture when he passed
that way in the seventh century preaching a benevolent Buddhism; while Nestorian Christians erected a monastery upon
its shores in the fourteenth century.

There are few trees around the lake, except those which border mountain streams. But on the eastern end the narrow plain which elsewhere separates lake from mountain lengthens fifty miles or more in a delightful valley, abounding with flowers, that has been the center of bee culture from immemorial times. A recent report gives the annual export of honey as 800 tons.

Fish are plentiful, for other records list the annual catch at 400 tons. The carp is commercially the most important variety.

Violent winds, sweeping down from the mountains, make the waters unsafe for small boats. The Russians, however, have introduced steamers which now connect local commerce with the west by caravans that toil laboriously over passes more than 12,000 feet high. At intervals in the surrounding mountain wall these windows to the outer world appear, ranging in elevation from 11,650 feet to over 14,000.

The region was annexed by Russia in 1864 and now forms part of the Kirghiz Republic in the vast patchwork quilt of diverse nationalities that make up the Red Empire. It remains, however, rich in historical associations, while doubtless many archaeological treasures still lie concealed along the lonely shores or beneath the fluctuating waters of Issyk-Kul.

BAIKAL, COLOSSUS OF FRESH WATERS

A gigantic gash cuts a remote tableland of Central Asia as with a Titan's blade. Filled with water, cold and beautifully clear, it reflects the tangled mountain peaks rising to a height of 5000 feet that surround it on every hand. Roving Mongols, gazing upon the mysterious mist that veils much of its surface in summer, called it Dalai Nor, the Holy Lake, but it is imperfectly known to the outside world as Baikal, perhaps the most interesting of fresh-water lakes.

First of all, it is immeasurably ancient. Where most lakes date only to the glacial age, geologists trace Baikal's origin to Jurassic times, tens of millions of years ago. It fills a fold or depression formed when much of the continent wrinkled into mountain chains and may, so earthquake shocks and other more superficial data indicate, actually be penetrating still further into the global substrata. This appalling gulf is the most abysmal on the land surface of the globe, for its floor is nearly 4000 feet below sea level. Death Valley, the Qattara Sink, and even the vast depression of the Dead Sea basin, reach no such "lows" as this. Hence Baikal is the deepest of lakes; lying at an elevation of 1515 feet, soundings have dipped through 5413 feet of water, or well over a mile.

Shaped somewhat like a flattened crescent, Baikal is 385 miles long with a maximum width of 46. Its area, 13,300 square miles, approximately that of Switzerland, ranks it as fifth among the world's fresh-water lakes. But in volume of waters it is indisputably first.

Superior, long regarded as number one, has an area of 31,810 square miles, seemingly a commanding lead. Moreover, as lakes go, it is also deep, one sounding recorded by the Hydrographic and Map Service of Ottawa registering 1302 feet. Its average depth, however, as given by the United States Lake Survey, is 487 feet. A Russian survey of Baikal in 1896 found but 8 per cent of the bottom within the 30-fathom line, while the 100-fathom mark (600 feet) ran close to shore. The average depth was about 700 meters, or just under 2300 feet. The conclusion seems inescapable. Although Baikal has little more than 41 per cent of Superior's area, it is nearly five times as deep. Hence its profound basin could accommodate not only Superior's waters but probably that of all five of the Great Lakes. Their combined volume has been estimated at 5430 cubic miles; Baikal's, according to available data, is 5785. In fact its volume exceeds that of the Baltic Sea. Allowing for various inaccuracies, for no survey of lacustrine basins is ever complete, Baikal must be recognized as the colossus of fresh-water reservoirs.

More than three hundred streams, mostly mountain torrents, pour into Baikal, their floods of melted snows causing the level to fluctuate three feet from April lows to September highs. There is also a curious ground swell called the zyb, whose cause has not been satisfactorily explained. Through a precipitous gorge near the western end the lake discharges into the lower Angara, a major tributary of the mighty Yenisei. Another great river, the Lena, curls an envious branch like the tentacle of an octopus around Baikal's northern shore, barred only by a few miles of mountainous watershed.

Aquatic life in Baikal, quite in keeping with other extraordinary features, has made it a vast aquarium of archaic forms. The surface waters swarm with minute plankton. More than half the known species of *Gammarus*, a primitive crustacean, are found in Baikal; while no fewer than 184 species of this singular creature occur nowhere else. Fish are abundant, particularly sturgeon, and the usually marine herring. One lake specimen, the *Comephorus*, resembles some of the bizarre types dredged from the Deep Sea, for Baikal in depth is quite oceanic. Another, called *Golomynka*, is a mass of fat which is used for train oil. Still more impressive are the seals, which constitute a considerable fishery. Just how they ever got there, more than a thousand miles from the nearest indentation of the Pacific and still farther from the Arctic Ocean, is a problem for the biologists. Perhaps they followed the stream bed of the Angara, when levels were lower and much of Asiatic lowlands still under the sea. In any case, their presence is unmistakable, although the length of their residence is beyond reasonable conjecture.

No lake in the world, according to W. Halbfass, so profoundly affects the climate of the surrounding terrain. Quite like a bit of midocean transported bodily to Asiatic highlands, it tempers June heats and December colds by over five degrees. Below the 100-fathom mark the waters record a temperature of 39, which remains fairly constant to the bottom. Hot springs gush forth in certain places, revealing the global energy which carved out this profound abyss, while in other places petroleum bubbles up.

Baikal freezes late in December or early January and remains so until the latter part of May. A touch of Siberian temperature congeals the ice to a depth of three feet or more, providing an excellent surface for winter sledges. In summer the heated air, in contact with the chill water, creates a mist that mantles the lake for weeks on end, so that one Russian expedition found it almost completely obscured from July 13 to August 1.

From remote times Baikal has served as a highway of commerce. Tea from China has always been an important item, while traffic in timber, cedar nuts, soda, and other commodities has been considerable. Such commerce has been greatly stimulated since the discovery of the lake by the Russians in 1643. Steamers were introduced in 1844. The great Trans-Siberian, most ambitious of railway undertakings, paused at the shores of Baikal for many years, while freight was transhipped to the opposite side. Powerful 4200-ton icebreakers, able to smash their way through ice more than three feet thick, toiled in winter to keep channels open, while great carriers embarked twenty-five freight cars at one time. More recently a right of way has been blasted out around the precipitous southern end of the lake to permit uninterrupted trackage.

Undoubtedly lake commerce will increase with the development of Asiatic Russia. The shores, strangely beautiful, may

yet attract considerable settlements, although at present the
nearest big city, Irkutsk, is more than fifty miles away, for
among all the lakes of the globe none presents more extraordinary features than this vast natural reservoir in the heart of
Asia.

VAN OF VANISHED EMPIRES

Armenians call their big lake Arissa Palus, but it is better
known as Van. Roughly pear-shaped, the long axis extends
from southwest to northeast for 80 miles, while the bulging
southern sector is 40 miles wide. The area is approximately
2000 square miles, the altitude 5260 feet or just under a mile.
Surface levels, however, fluctuate eight feet or more over a
five-year cycle.

The waters are highly mineralized, containing, according
to Chancourtois, 22.6 grams of mineral per liter compared
with the Atlantic's 35.06. Alkaline rather than saline, they are
bitter to the taste. F. W. Clarke places Van in his ninth category of "non-fresh" water lakes under the heading of "triple
waters," as they are rich in all three combinations—chlorides,
sulphates, and carbonates. They contain so much borax that
the natives evaporate a crude residue for use as washing
powder.

Notwithstanding its complex chemical composition, the
waters abound with fish which are the basis of a considerable
industry. Prominent among species is a marine herring.

Several streams empty into the lake, while springs gush from
the hillsides. All about lies a loftier terrain with a jagged sky
line of extinct volcanoes. On the west the huge Nimrod crater
gapes five miles or more, while toward the north Sipan Dagh
frowns down from its height of 13,700 feet. Seventy miles

toward the northwest looms still loftier Ararat, 16,946 feet
high, the traditional resting place of Noah's Ark. Around the
southern coast steep hills, once densely forested, now present
a bleak and forsaken appearance. Here the landscape is dominated by Agherov Dagh, 11,000 feet high, guarding the
threshold of Kurdistan, in whose deep valleys nomads feed
their flocks and pitch their black tents.

About a mile from the eastern shore is the city of Van. Its
flat-roofed mud houses and crooked, narrow streets form an
amphitheater around Citadel Rock, an isolated ridge rising 360
feet above the plain. Winters are severe, as the snowfall averages from 2 to 3 feet.

Van is an ancient center on the Persian trade route to the
Far East, although commerce now trends northward through
Erzurum to Trebizond on the Black Sea. All about lie relics
of vanished empires. The lake was the center of the ancient
kingdom of Urartu, or Urutu, which battled Assur for
supremacy in the days of Assyrian greatness. The origin of its
people is shrouded in a fog of speculation. They seem to have
come from the western seacoasts rather than from interior
Asia, as their culture shows a kinship with the Minoan of
Crete, and their pottery resembles that of the Etruscans of
northern Italy, another racial enigma. Among the odd relics
so far recovered is a figurine of a bearded bison, once native to
this region.

From such vestiges archaeologists have traced the vague
outlines of a people called Urartu-Chaldian, not to be confused
with the Chaldean of Babylonia. A king of ancient Urartu
built an aqueduct 75 miles long which still bears water to Van's
arid eastern coast, while native artisans perfected a superior
quality of steel.

Somewhere about the year 714 B.C. savage Cimmerian tribes
broke through the passes of the Caucasus to ravage the country, while it has been overrun successively by the Persians,

Alexander the Great, the Romans, the Parthians, the Persians again under the aggressive Shapur, the emperors of Byzantium, and lastly by the Turks.

Van has been commercially active from prehistoric times. Many sailboats skim its blue surface, some engaged in fishing, some in transporting freight, although sudden storms make navigation perilous. Wheat and timber are the bulky items in a heterogeneous assortment of commodities.

Van is in Turkish territory, uncomfortably close to the Armenian Republic of the Soviets. To the north are discontented Armenians, to the south freedom-loving but lawless Kurds, while in the offing looms the red shadow of Russia. Perhaps political unrest is normal in a region which has so often witnessed the conflict of empires and remains a vortex of discordant races.

PULSATING LAKE URMIA

In the northeastern corner of Iran lies a singular body of water called Urmia. It occupies a shallow depression in an extensive tableland at an elevation of 4184 feet above the sea. In this depression the outlines of the lake pulsate in so extraordinary a manner that during the past century its length has varied from 80 to 90 miles, its width from 30 to 45. Its maximum area has been calculated at 2317 square miles, while even its minimum, 1544, entitles it to entry among the world's big lakes.

Such fluctuations make the lake a treacherous neighbor. In 1897 an Italian expedition found the rising waters had inundated many cultivated fields and threatened several shore settlements. Again, over considerable periods, the waters have subsided, exposing salt-encrusted mud flats steaming with smelly hydrogen sulphide. Urmia is certainly temperamental.

In many respects it resembles Great Salt Lake, whose shore lines are also subject to wide disturbances. Its waters are nearly seven times saltier than those of Lake Van, with a mineral content, according to F. W. Clarke, of 148,500 parts per 1,000,-000. He placed it in Class I among his nine divisions of lakes with a solution of chlorides, sulphates, and carbonates roughly paralleling those in the sea. Bathers find it impossible to sink in its waters, which are refreshing, although they inflame the eyes and throat.

Several rivers flow into Urmia, the largest the Djaghaty, draining a considerable area toward the south. Smaller streams disappear in the thirsty ground. Fish of surprising length, five feet or more, lurk in the mouths of such streams as reach the lake, but no fish could endure its acrid waters, where only a few shrimp and larval insects survive.

The surrounding scenery is lofty and imposing. Mount Sahend, thirty miles to the northeast, towers 11,630 feet, while more distant Savalan, 15,792 feet high, retains its snowy covering until late summer. To the south one peak juts up 11,350 feet, while a mountain range toward the west reaches heights of 13,675. These all form a splendid setting for shallow, varicolored Urmia.

Although the lake occupies part of an isolated drainage basin of about 20,000 square miles, it may have been a gulf of the Sarmatian sea in Miocene times, as the Caspian, toward the east, is scarcely two hundred miles distant. R. T. Günther, near the close of the past century, found relics of corals, echinoderms, and other marine species in the old lake bed. He also thought the waters had recently overspread 600 additional square miles. The islands toward the south shore, which number fifty or more, impressed him greatly. The largest of these, Koyun Daghi, three or four miles long, made a striking appearance, with its white chalk cliffs mirrored in the turquoise water. Fresh springs overflowed the marshy shores where natives found pasturage for their goats. A much larger island called Shahi lies in the northern section, as Urmia's major axis runs roughly north and south.

A dozen miles from the western shore is the ancient city of Urmia, which the natives pronounce Urmi. It is situated in a fertile valley amid orchards extending for miles. Streams of fresh water traverse the principal streets. The city was long a center of the Nestorian Christians. Across the lake and thirty miles farther to the northeast is the city of Tabriz, famous for its bazaars. Marco Polo shrewdly noted that its "merchants make large profits." The Mongol Hulagu, ferocious grandson of Genghis Khan, was fond of this region, and ornate tombs mark the graves of members of his family.

The prevalent religion is Islamism, colored by Aryan influence. Although Mohammed, like the ancient Hebrews, forbade the reproduction in art of any living object, a taboo which stimulated the creation of arabesque designs, devout Persians weave birds and flowers into the patterns of their rugs and carpets.

The region is not only a vortex of alien faiths, but the cradle of an Old World religion. Upon a nearby hill called Bakchi-kala stood the traditional city of Zoroaster. This great teacher, who antedated Buddha and Confucius, gave the world a noble faith in which embattled virtue, personified in Ormuzd, the divinity of goodness and light, strove for the mastery of the universe with Ahriman, the evil spirit of darkness. This religion is still revered by the Parsees of India, sometimes, though erroneously, known as fire worshipers.

Motorboats, connecting commerce with neighboring railways, add a modern touch to Urmia, but the picturesque native craft seem more appropriate. Round-bottomed, with flat sterns, and equipped with a single mast carrying a square sail, they can progress only before the wind. When this changes, down goes the huge iron anchor to safeguard prog-

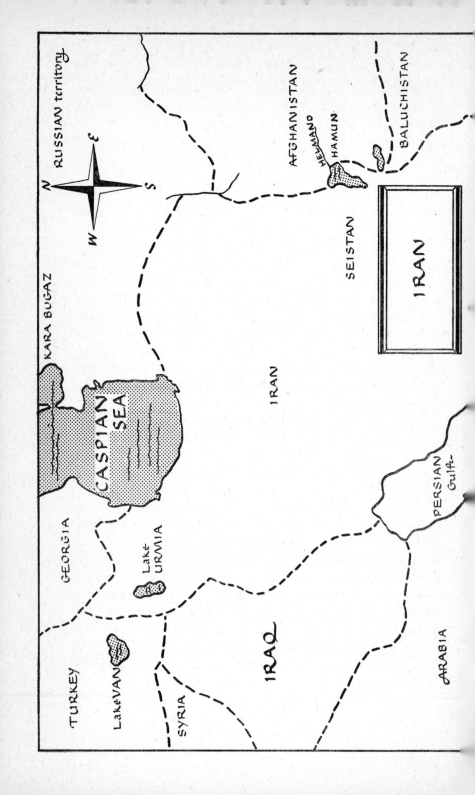

ress made until a favoring breeze insures another advance. Such navigation is possible in these shallow waters, seldom over fifteen feet deep and never more than fifty.

In the broad basin a rise of a few inches means an overflow of many square miles. Nevertheless, changing lake contours have sometimes been ascribed to readjustments in the underlying strata. Queer manifestations do occur, for Dr. Willis, who spent some time in the vicinity, was amazed one night to see dancing sheets of flame burst from the surface of the lake. Uncertain what caused so extraordinary a display, he was inclined to suspect an exhibition of the familiar marsh fire upon a gigantic scale, due to some chemical reaction. For Urmia is a huge vat of minerals in solution, seething with restless gases.

No less disturbed is the political situation, for the big lake lies in the province of Azerbaijan, where Russian influence clashes with the unstable Iranian government. Here the negative creed of Communism seems to be supplanting the ancient ritual of the Magi, and may also engulf other cherished faiths in the red tide of atheism.

THE WEIRD SEISTAN

Span the width of Iran by a line running southeastward for nearly a thousand miles, and we come to one of the strangest lake regions on earth. It lies on the border between Persia and Afghanistan, shut off from the Persian Gulf, three hundred miles away, by lofty mountain ranges. Known as the Seistan, it is a vast depression of 7000 square miles that receives the waters of an interior drainage system almost twenty times as extensive.

The northern sector of this depression is the lake region. Here a shallow body of water called Hamun-i-Sabari sprawls over an indeterminate area that sometimes reaches impressive dimensions. According to the map of Mr. Tate, based upon surveys early in the present century, it stretches well over 100 miles, a crescent with an area of 2000 square miles. Upon another map, however, appearing in 1928, it seemed to have split in two, the larger portion assuming a mushroom shape about 35 miles long. Its waters, nowhere over ten feet deep, were drinkable, while dense thickets of rushes fringed the shifting borders. By a winding channel known as the Shelaz this lake connected with a smaller though considerable body of water farther south, the Gaud-i-Zirreh, its main axis slanting roughly 60 miles east and west, its maximum breadth about 20.

Among the several streams which drain into the Seistan is the Helmand, the largest Asiatic river between the Tigris and the Indus. Rising in the lofty plateau of Afghanistan, it rushes downward for 600 miles, bearing the melted snows of towering mountain ranges. In floodtime it pours a turbulent torrent into the Hamun at the rate of 700,000 cubic feet a second, or more than twice the normal outflow of the five Great Lakes into the St. Lawrence River. Though clear and pure at its source, accumulated products of erosion make it one of the siltiest rivers on earth. This rich sediment would, it has been estimated, annually cover ten square miles a foot deep. Nowhere else, save in the Nile Valley, is there such a combination of inexhaustible water supply and boundless fertility.

And yet the Seistan is a fearsome region where life survives under incredible difficulties. Sir Henry McMahon, who conducted its survey for two and a half years, has left vivid recollections. Through the sweltering summer a violent wind blows almost continuously across the depression from May until September. Its direction, from a little west of north, never seems to vary; its velocity sometimes exceeds seventy miles per hour, a screaming gale, angry with driven dust. Emerging from the so-called Desert of Despair to the north, it has gouged out great holes two hundred feet deep. Elsewhere it strews the ground with vast windrows, while in between it sweeps like a gigantic broom, revealing new surfaces of fertile soil. In fact the whole Seistan may have been partially, if not wholly, eroded by what the natives call this "Hundred and Twenty Day Wind."

Yet such atmospheric frenzy is not an unmixed evil. It tempers summer heats that rise to 122 in the shade and carries away innumerable insects that breed in the swamps. One of these is a kind of gadfly infected with a germ fatal to horses. As a protection, the English surveyors clothed their steeds in grotesque pajamas.

The sinister combination of fierce winds, scorching heat, and insect irritation drives animals literally mad. The jackals, which together with wild pigs infest the reedy delta of the Helmand, not infrequently develop hydrophobia and go raving about the countryside. Two wolves, thus afflicted, bit seventy-eight camels attached to the expedition; forty of the unfortunate creatures that developed the dread disease had to be shot.

Winter also has its problems. The thermometer may sink nearly to zero, much of the lake surface freezes over, and icy gales attain even more ungovernable violence. In one March storm which lasted nearly four days, the winds reached a velocity of 120 miles per hour. Over two hundred camels perished, while nearly five thousand of these sturdy beasts succumbed to hardship during the entire stay of the party. Even springtime, the happiest, or rather the least distressing, period of the year, revives not only insect pests but swarms of serpents, many poisonous.

Under such conditions the lot of the surveyor is a trying one. A party of Anglo-Indians, venturing into a blank space on the map, found a waterless region where even their camels perished of thirst. One by one the members of the party, eight

in all, staggering back on foot, dropped in their tracks. The
sole survivor, delirious but still clutching the precious survey,
fell unconscious beside a water hole, whence he was rescued
by an Afghan nomad.

A more inhospitable region would be difficult to picture,
yet the Seistan has a romantic past that trails away beyond the
horizons of recorded history. It was the traditional home of
Rustam, the Hercules of Persian Myth, who not only fought
armies but withstood dragons and demons. It was the home of
the founders of the illustrious line of Persian kings which num-
bered Cyrus and Darius and Xerxes, and became one of the
original satrapies of the vast Persian Empire. Alexander the
Great traversed the Seistan on his way to India. For a time it
was overrun by wild Scythian tribes from the north; again
Mahmud of Ghazni, one of the heroes of the Mohammedan
world, added it to his other conquests. It was ravaged by the
Mongol raiders of Genghis Khan, while that saturnine genius,
Timur, completed its destruction. It was here that he received
the arrow in the leg which changed his name to Timur the
Lame, our familiar Tamerlane; here, too, he wreaked fearful
vengeance by not only slaughtering the inhabitants and
destroying their cities, but breaking up the irrigation canals
that once made the Seistan another fertile Babylonia. Perhaps
it was this injury, so corroding to his savage temper, that
explains the later act of his when he reared outside the city of
Bagdad a pyramid of 70,000 human skulls! More recently
Nadir Shah, the last great Persian potentate, also overran the
Seistan.

Scattered throughout the region are innumerable ruins. In
one section explorers found them stretching for thirty miles.
Sir Aurel Stein, on his visit in 1915, excavated a hill covered
with shattered Buddhist temples and monasteries overlying
Sassanid and older relics identified as Hellenic. Mounds of
former villages are everywhere blackened with fires and clut-

tered with broken pottery. Here also are found not a few mementos of the Stone Age. For in a bone-dry atmosphere, where the annual precipitation is less than 3 inches, trophies of the past survive almost as well as in Egypt.

The future of the region depends upon a wise utilization of the Helmand River, which continues to pour out its floods and fertilizing silt. Several times its broad delta has shifted; every few years (natives say in cycles of seven) torrential rains swell its volume until the Hamun overflows its reedy banks to become one of the great lakes of the world. If science cannot bridle the ungovernable winds, it might irrigate the basin, control insect pests, and temper a climate now little less than appalling. For a region so rich in historic tradition, endowed with boundless natural resources, need not always remain poverty-stricken and over half depopulated.

CHINA'S CURIOUS LAKES

1. Tung Ting

Although China boasts no major lakes, she has several invested with a peculiar charm or unusual history. As a type of the former, we might glance for a moment at Tung Ting Lake, beloved of many emperors.

It lies far in the interior, in the crowded province of Hunan. The largest lake in China proper, it is but one of many that strew the broad valley of the Yangtze River and maintain a unique partnership with that great artery of commerce.

Lake and river are united by two canals. In summer floods the river overflows until Tung Ting's flexible borders expand to a length of 75 and a width of 60 miles. But in winter the lake ebbs back into the river until much of its bed is exposed and many new islands appear.

Because of its irregular shore line, the Chinese distinguish such divisions as the Green Grass Lake, the Red Sand Lake, and others equally appropriate. Its communal name, however, is the Lake of the Nine Rivers. Among these numerous affluents are the Yuen-kiang and the much larger Siang-kiang which floods the bottom with vast quantities of silt so that the eastern shores are very shallow.

Albert Bickmore, who visited the region eighty years ago, has left this word picture: "As far as the eye could see, the lake was feathered with white sails busily engaged in transporting tea, timber, coal, and various other commodities. I counted 440 at one time—a beautiful sight." Of the lake he wrote: "The shore line is irregular and there are many islands." In this densely peopled land the countryside is crowded with buildings ranging from gilded pagodas and the summer pavilions of mandarins to the huts of humble fishermen—a cross section of the Orient in one of its most picturesque settings.

One lake curiosity is a species of dolphin found nowhere else. Long ago it ventured up the Yangtze from the far-off Pacific, found the surroundings congenial, and has remained ever since. The Chinese are proud of this ocean vagrant which preferred their lake to its ancestral home.

2. Koko Nor

Far different is the lake called Koko Nor.

Tucked away in the northeast corner, it is a little over a hundred miles inside the Great Wall of China, and west of the province of Kansu. Unlike Tung Ting, it is entirely isolated, though a branch of the treacherous Yellow River, called because of its devastating floods China's Sorrow, approaches within a few miles.

On the maps the lake is pear-shaped and some 75 by 40 miles in extent. From the northeast it receives the Bukhain Gol, most considerable of its tributary streams. Here the country is wilder, swept by the great winds of Central Asia, and sparsely settled. The lake waters, according to C. Schmidt, are about one third as salt as the ocean, abound with fish, and have been called very beautiful.

The Russian Captain Kozloff visited the region in 1907. Disregarding tales that the lake was devil-haunted and that wood sank beneath its surface, he brought with him a collapsible boat. Curious about the sacred island of Kuisu, whose rocky heights towered 200 feet above the center of the lake, he found the only inhabitants were three anchorites who lived in caves and subsisted upon cheese and other dairy products from their small herds. They gazed upon him with stupefaction, as though he were a supernatural being, for no other foreigner had ever invaded their cloistered solitude.

Walter C. Lowdermilk, who visited Koko Nor a few years ago, estimated its elevation at about 10,000 feet and called it "a gem of sapphire set in an emerald basin bordered by green-clad mountains capped with snow." He thought its area might approximate 1600 square miles, but it has never been surveyed.

3. Lop Nor

A much stranger lake lies beyond the Astin Tagh Mountains to the northeast. This branch of the vast Kunlun range shuts off Tibet to form an extensive drainage basin stretching east and west for 900 miles, with an extreme width of perhaps 350. Toward its narrow western end, the Kunlun bars the outer world with such imposing giants as Muztagh Ata, 24,388 feet high, and the still loftier Kungur, 25,146. On its northern border the Tien Shan or Celestial Mountains edge the sky line with their never melting snows. Though not quite so formidable as the Kunlun, they culminate in Tengri Khan at a height of 23,620 feet, hundreds of feet above the loftiest peak in the western hemisphere. Beyond them, toward the northwest, is the valley of the Issyk-Kul and the region of the Balkhash.

Gripped between these two gigantic mountain ranges, the valley narrows toward the west, where the cities of Kashgar and Yarkand stand as outposts of a different civilization, while in the remote distance, beyond breath-taking passes, beckon the gardens of the Oxus and Jaxartes and the plains of the Aral Sea.

Down this valley from the west flows the restless Tarim River, nearly a thousand miles in length, to lose itself in the lowest part of the depression, where lie the beds of migratory lakes. Here Sir Aurel Stein came upon a region some 165 miles long by 90 broad, furrowed by icy winds into clay ridges coated with salt that resembled breakers in a frozen sea. The Chinese call these weird formations white dragon mounds, and see in them crouching monsters. Camels, in crossing this uncanny wilderness, occasionally break through the salt crust and, according to native reports, are swallowed up in soft mud.

Through the Tarim Valley, for thousands of years, intermittent traffic between China and the Western World has followed two great silk routes. Marco Polo, who took the southern route, described the city of Lop as "situated toward the northeast, near the commencement of a great desert," adding, "It is a well-known fact that the desert is the abode of many evil spirits." True, he neglected to mention the neighboring lake, but he also forgot to speak of China's Great Wall, which he must have crossed several times.

A Russian expedition visiting this region in 1890 found a lake surrounded by clay covered with salt. Through a channel 13 miles long flowed the Tarim River, which became slightly salt in the shallows. The southern portion of the lake, 7 miles in diameter, seemed free from reeds, though its waters were so bitter that even thirsty camels refused to drink them.

This vacant attic of the world, with its vast solitudes and

terrifying manifestations, has been explored by Sven Hedin on a number of expeditions. On one of these he avoided starvation by resorting to such dubious eatables as grass and coagulated blood, and rather envied the camels which, when utterly spent, lay down to gaze sphinxlike over the desert while awaiting death with true oriental resignation.

Hedin first found the Tarim emptying into a lake called Kara Koshun (presumably that of the Russian expedition). As this was far from the position of Lop Nor on ancient Chinese maps, he followed a dry channel of the Tarim to another lake bed to the north. Here in a ruined city (probably ancient Lop) he unearthed many documents, some on wood, some on paper, relics of a former trade center of considerable importance. On a more recent tour he discovered that the Tarim exit into Kara Koshun was rapidly silting up while the river, reverting to its former channel, seemed engaged in refilling the old lake bed. He believes this is the true Lop Nor of antiquity, and makes the bold claim that the capricious stream oscillates from one lake to the other, so that Lop Nor is alternately abandoned and revived over cycles of fifteen hundred years.

This singular body of water, well termed the Wandering Lake, is north of Tibet in the great province of Sinkiang, which stretches far into the interior of Asia. Though technically under Chinese domination, Russian influence has so far infiltrated that the boundaries of empire seem as unstable as the shores of Lop Nor beside its wilderness of wind-eroded salt.

THE SKY LAKES OF TIBET

Certain extensive areas are definite lake regions. In the most notable of these, the Great Canadian Shield, innumerable lakes were carved out by the continental icecap. A corresponding, but similar, icecap explains Finland's 60,000 lakes, while the Russian explorer, Prince Kropotkin, thought the legions of lakes that sprinkle the steppes in the Aral-Balkhash region were also due to glacial action. Many of these are more probably of oceanic origin, remnants of that vast Eurasian Mediterranean which still survives in the Aral and the Caspian. These lake areas all lie at a relatively low elevation.

Some big lakes in both Africa and Asia show a considerable altitude due to upheavals in the earth crust, while Titicaca in South America was evidently lifted bodily by the enormous upsurge of the Andes. But the numerous lakes of Tibet are unique, immured as they are by giant mountain ranges and scattered over the most extensive plateau on earth.

This stupendous tableland has an elevation of about 14,000 feet. The landscape alternates between rounded ridges, which offer scant protection from the bitter winds, and broad valleys that provide shallow basins for numerous lakes. A few of these are fresh-water, a few brackish, but the great majority are saline. Replenished by scanty rainfall or the melted snows of mountains, they survive in a hostile environment to add a forlorn note of beauty to a landscape singularly barren and austere. That their struggle for existence is a losing one, however, is revealed by the salt pans and borax fields which mark the site of former lakes.

The history of these fugitive bodies of water is obscure. Colonel Meinertzhagen doubted their glacial origin, as he was sure that Tibet's limited rainfall would never have permitted the accumulation of any considerable ice field. A contrary view, however, was advanced by Dr. Emil Trinkler, who explored the region in 1927. He thought he could detect evidences of just such an ice field all the way from the Indus River to the vast ranges of the Tien Shan.

Since the hermit kingdom so long maintained a frigid isolation, only vague rumors reached the world about its lakes. A typical example is Tengri Nor, less than a hundred miles northwest of Lhasa, the forbidden capital of the Dalai Lama. It was first sighted in 1872 by Hindu pandits in the employ of the Trigonometrical Survey of India who, disguised as merchants or religious pilgrims, and at peril of their lives, explored the recesses of high Asia. They ascertained that the elevation of the lake was 15,190 feet, or just under three miles, and estimated its length at 50 miles, its breadth at 35. The Lama Nan-Cho informed them that its highly descriptive name was "the Sky Lake."

In 1875 C. F. Markham approached the region through a thermal field of hot springs where at least two geysers spouted steaming water, the larger to a height of 60 feet. A scanty scrub grew on the barren slopes, but the lake shores were uninhabited save for three isolated Buddhist monasteries. The waters, heavily saline, contained many fish, though no one seemed to catch them. From early fall till late spring the lake was a sheet of ice.

Later expeditions added further information. The borders of a larger lake were traced in neighboring beaches and many mollusk shells unearthed. Tengri Nor seems to have been visited long ago by Jesuit missionaries, and was dimly known to the Chinese as the Lake of Heaven, presumably because of its sky-blue color and the majestic mountains that surround it. These are dominated by three great peaks all over 21,000 feet in height, all crusted with never melting snows, the largest resembling a titanic block of white marble. Few lakes have a lonelier or more impressive setting.

Tibetans have developed customs in conformity with their cheerless climate. Bathing is strictly taboo, hence they become more greasy and filthy than the most degraded Eskimos. Among their garments, necessarily warm, sheepskins predominate. That curious reversal of polygamy known as polyandry has its stronghold in Tibet, where males far outnumber females.

Food is a perennial problem. As grains grow sparsely upon their high uplands, Tibetans subsist largely upon mutton and the flesh of the yak, that grotesque animal which thrives at such altitudes. Yaks are nearly as vital to their economy as are camels in Arabia, for not only are they beasts of burden, but they supply leather, flesh, and milk. From the latter the natives churn a crude kind of butter, which they mix with tea imported in bricks from China, and are so fond of the soupy mixture, plentifully flavored with dirt and yak hairs, that they drink upward of fifty cups a day. Though Buddhism is the avowed religion, that noble faith, corrupted by native superstitions, has degenerated into a form but little better than devil worship. The more learned lamas are adept in various feats of legerdemain which savor of the black art of the Middle Ages. The devils, however, which they seek to appease by gifts and incantations, have a real existence in ignorance and credulity fostered by a stubborn national pride and aloofness, and nourished in a sterile soil, chill winds, and a landscape of profound melancholy.

A typical border lake is Pangong, which lies mainly in Kashmir, though it projects into Tibet. Caught up in the gigantic folds of the Karakoram range, it has an elevation of 13,915 feet. Some 50 miles long by 10 broad (dimensions are largely estimates) it has been described as more deeply blue than the Mediterranean off the Riviera. Tremendous peaks are mirrored on its surface, one rising more than 21,000 feet only to be overtopped by another across the valley over 22,000 feet high. Curious lagoons which seem deeper than the lake itself fringe its shores, shut off by sand bars cast up by the waves. A recent expedition found the surface levels rising as several islands were wholly submerged and an ancient road led into the lake. Many prayer wheels erected along the shores by Buddhist pilgrims had been ruined by the advancing waters.

Pangong has no outlet, though one may once have existed, for a branch of the aggressive Indus approaches within a few miles. Scattered hill dwellers inhabit the region; the waters abound with fish, while other forms of wild life include snow leopards and fleet wild asses.

Tibetan lakes are commercially valueless save for their mineral deposits. They once supplied Europe with its borax under the trade name of tincal. That desolate plateau, bleak as it is, would be even more forbidding if they did not temper, to some degree, the parching winds that fret its sullen loneliness.

THE DESOLATE DEAD SEA

The Great African Rift has created many lakes. Some are among the world's largest, where faulted valleys have deepened into abysmal Tanganyika and Nyasa. But nowhere are they more intriguing than in Palestine, where the Rift has plowed a gigantic furrow from the Lebanon Mountains southward.

Here lies the Sea of Galilee, a pear-shaped body of water 13 miles long by 8 wide. It partially fills a vast bowl surrounded by steep hills that on the east ascend abruptly. According to Lortet, its maximum soundings are about 150 feet. Fish abound in its slightly brackish waters, where the leading Apostles cast their nets, a fact commemorated in a member of the finny tribe still known as St. Peter's fish. But the outstanding characteristic of the waters is their altitude, or rather lack of it, for they lie nearly 700 feet below the surface of the Mediterranean, scarcely twenty-five miles away. Other evidences of a gigantic dislocation of earth's strata appear in thermal springs which bubble forth near the ancient city of Tiberias.

The lake is hardly beautiful, although pilgrims have sought

to invest it with exaggerated loveliness. But it has a stronger appeal enshrined in the historic background of Christianity.

The river Jordan, flowing southward from lesser pools and the springs of Hermon, enters the lake, then issues forth from the southern extremity to go hurrying down the Rift valley. The distance is only sixty-five miles, but it makes many devious twistings in descending an average of nine feet per mile. No other river, except subterranean streams, lies so far below sea level; no other, except the Ganges, is so revered. Fairly clear in its upper reaches, it becomes increasingly muddy until it loses itself in the Dead Sea.

From remotest times this enormous sink has been regarded as the absolute nadir of desolation. To be sure, a few visitors have been charmed by the wild and rugged terrain toward the south, but to the majority it has seemed weird and almost uncanny. The Sea, 47 miles long with an extreme width of 9½, has an area of 340 square miles. Eastward rise the Mountains of Moab, while the wilderness of Judea to the west is quite as lofty and even more barren. The lake fills only a portion of a more extensive bed whose exposed mud flats are blotched with alkali. The waters have been described as deeply blue, but near shore they resemble soapy wash water to which a liberal admixture of bluing has been added, certainly more suggestive of turquoise than sapphire. They are so dense that a swimmer cannot sink, but bobs about like a cork and may become topheavy, while they burn both eyes and throat and crack shoe leather. Their mineral content is 245.73 grams per liter, or more than seven times that of the Atlantic. F. W. Clarke lists the Dead Sea in the second of his nine divisions of mineralized lakes as a natural bittern, for its waters are alkaline rather than saline, and the predominance of magnesium compounds imparts a bitter taste. While common salt (sodium chloride) comprises 77.7 per cent of the mineral content of the oceans, the percentage falls to 33.4 in the Dead Sea. Magnesium chloride, however, is proportionately four times as abundant, accounting for nearly 42 per cent of all solids in solution. According to J. B. Philby, more than 2,000,000,000 tons of magnesium and other chlorides are dissolved in the Dead Sea, salts enough to form a single lump with a volume of four cubic miles. A foreign concession has been engaged for some years in retrieving the wealth of mineral from this liquid mine.

In the southern sector a curious peninsula known as El Lisan (the tongue) projects from the Mountains of Moab halfway across the lake. It rises to a height of about fifty feet, though the isthmus is low and marshy. Points on this forlorn land mass are named for two early explorers: Costigan, who came here in 1825, and Molyneux, who came in 1847. Both lost their lives in the course of their explorations.

North of this ill-starred peninsula soundings record a depth of 1278 feet. As the lake surface is 1292 feet below the sea, the profoundest open space on earth, its bottom recesses are 2570 beneath sea level, or three hundred feet deeper than Tanganyika's. Only Lake Baikal probes farther into the earth crust. South of the peninsula the waters become very shallow, ranging from 3 to 12 feet. In the dismal salt and gypsum desert still farther south various formations have been identified as Lot's wife. Here also flourished the fabulous Dead Sea fruit of the Middle Ages, which was pleasing to the sight but crumbled to dust at the touch. Somewhere in this eerie valley or beneath the waters of the lake, according to Josephus, lie the ruins of those ultrawicked cities, Sodom and Gomorrah.

But the Dead Sea is extraordinary enough without borrowing from the supernatural. There are electrical disturbances which have not been wholly explained. Queer, also, are the lines of foam which streak its surface. These seem to follow the major axis, which runs nearly north and south. Mr. Ashbel found they appeared in the morning to spread out later in vast fan-shaped outlines. He thought they might be caused by springs of water of lesser specific gravity, gushing from the mountains or perhaps by the current of the Jordan, whose daily influx is estimated at 6,000,000 tons. They have also been ascribed to emanations from subterranean fissures.

Asphalt deposits about the Dead Sea are so noticeable that Josephus called the lake itself Asphaltitis. The earthquake of 1834 released large masses of bitumen which drifted ashore, but whether these resulted from tectonic action or were mere accumulations washed down by neighboring streams is uncertain.

The Dead Sea was never commercially important. The few boats mentioned by Tacitus have long since disappeared. Birds seldom frequent its evil waters, giving rise to stories of poisonous miasmas, for the very breath of the Dead Sea was supposedly fatal. A more scientific explanation lies in the absence of aquatic life.

Mr. Irwin thought the Dead Sea was not over fifty thousand years old. Its surface has fluctuated greatly, for even a single decade, 1930–1940, showed a subsidence of over twelve feet with an added density of mineral content. Whether such aberrations are caused by a lessening inflow, a more rapid evaporation, or are linked with a further collapse of underlying rock strata is debatable. For the latter explanation is by no means improbable in what has been called the most unstable valley in the world.

VI

Australian Lakes

THE GREAT AUSTRALIAN RIFT

One of the queerest lake regions on earth is found in South Australia. These lakes are shallow, salt, and of uncertain boundary and volume. Most of them are playas, where moisture accumulates only at intervals; or dismal saline marshes; or dry salt pans, mere vacant impressions where lakes have been. For they lie in that area of blistering heat and parching winds of emptiness and silence, the never-never land that sheepherders call the "back of beyond."

Much of this region is tectonic and often referred to as the Great Australian Rift. Unlike its more famous African prototype, where gigantic trenches are thousands of feet deep, the sinking here was less profound and involved wide areas rather than narrow strips. Recent Pliocene times, so geologists believe, witnessed the complicated warping and faulting which laid the groundwork for these strange lakes. Then the even coast line of the Great Australian Bight was invaded by long sea tongues in Spencer and St. Vincents gulfs, which penetrated much farther inland than they do today, while Kangaroo Island, the Yorke Peninsula, and the Flinders Mountains, culminating in peaks over 4000 feet high, emerged in a corresponding global readjustment.

At least one of these lakes, Torrens, was a portion of the sea recaptured when the intervening terrain uptilted once more, for it is a continuation of Spencer Gulf, into which it has drained intermittently within recorded time. But farther inland a vast fresh-water lake accumulated which some investigators hold may have been 1200 miles long by 700 broad, dwarfing even those glacial mammoths Algonquin and Agassiz and Ojibway of North America. More probably there were several lakes, though much larger than present shore lines indicate, in what was destined to become a great interior basin.

The rainfall must have been far heavier then. Along beaches clothed in verdure roamed prehistoric kangaroos and wombats, while the shallows swarmed with crocodiles which perished as the waters grew saline or evaporated. For a climate which grew progressively arid has proved quite as decisive in the history of these lakes as the original dislocation of the earth crust.

Australia's west coast is bathed by a cool ocean current. Winds chilled by this great river of the sea blow inland and, expanding, not only yield little moisture but absorb what remains upon the drying earth. Toward the southwest low but broad mountain masses prove an effective barrier to rain clouds, while on the south ocean gulfs are too narrow to provide humidity. And so the continent has become a shell of fertile territory surrounding a sun-scorched interior where over 1,000,000 square miles the annual rainfall is less than 10 inches. Quite as unfortunate is the erratic nature of this rainfall, which may appear in a single downpour, only to be followed by several seasons without a drop of moisture. One inland station reported but 6 inches of rainfall in ten years! No wonder camels, inured to hardships, have been known to travel fifteen days without a drink, or that, according to the Meteorological Bureau, an area of 800,000 square miles supports a white population of less than one thousand persons!

As the rainfall declines, the rate of evaporation increases. At Laverton it is 146 inches annually, over fifteen times the average rainfall. What chances have lakes to survive under such conditions? Even rivers become impoverished streams that slink into the sands or degenerate into Arabian-like wadis. The largest barely escape this humiliating fate. The one great river system of Australia, the Murray-Darling, is 2310 miles long, with a drainage basin of 414,000 square miles. Yet it is subject to the most extraordinary fluctuations. In 1870 the Darling overflowed to become a shallow lake 60 miles wide; in 1902–03, for a space of eleven months, it ceased to flow at all. Less than 10 per cent of the rainfall over its upper areas ever reaches the sea. The Murray, through the final five hundred miles of its course, not only receives no further increment but loses much of its original volume. Such scant rainfall as does occur seems to recoil from the sluggish current to be sucked up by the thirsty earth. Hence in dry seasons the stream is choked with sand bars and becomes too salt for cattle to drink. At the last this noble river, depleted and spiritless, loses itself in shallow Lake Alexandrina, some 12 by 30 miles in extent, whence it overflows spasmodically into the sea. Within recent years, however, the Australian government has constructed a series of dams or weirs to maintain water levels.

In this environment of inadequate and capricious rainfall, of anemic rivers and dead or dying lakes, Australians have turned to artesian wells. Several borings in Queensland furnish a daily flow of 3,000,000 gallons. One, the Bimerah No. 3, is 5045 feet, or nearly a mile, in depth. Its waters, heated by the earth's internal fires, register 190 degrees. Unfortunately the water table which underlies the vast lake district is predominantly saline. Only in restricted areas do expensive drilling operations tap sweet springs, while many prove too salt or alkaline to use. It almost seems that nature has wreaked vengeance upon the land after the manner of the biblical king who not only destroyed a city but sowed it with salt. Yet such arid regions, if unsuited to agriculture and doubtful as pasturage, are rich in minerals. Glamorous gold rushes have marked each discovery of the yellow metal, while prosaic salt and gypsum may prove at once more dependable and more inexhaustible sources of wealth.

In 1829 the schooner *Henry*, loading sealskins and kangaroo hides, carried off twenty tons of salt scraped from the earth on Kangaroo Island. Such surface mining has been widely followed. As a lake dries up in summer, the mineral covering is scraped from the exposed bottom and the process repeated at some future time. The operation is profitable where the deposit is a half inch deep. This crust is renewed in a singular manner, as described in the Geological Survey of South Australia. "The source of a considerable proportion of the salt now concentrated into workable deposits or in the ground water is due to salt occurring as dust in the air." This "cyclic" salt is merely ocean spray dried into minute particles and finely diffused, to be borne inland by the winds. Tests of rainwater samples reveal its presence as winter storms rinse it from the air to accumulate in shallow depressions which serve as drying pans. Hence Australia's salt and bitter lakes, if good for little else, are efficient collectors of minerals.

LAKE TORRENS

Torrens appears on early maps of South Australia as a vast lake curving inland for four hundred miles from the head of Spencer Gulf. Sometimes likened to a horseshoe, it rather resembled a gigantic question mark on the threshold of the unknown.

Later explorations have broken up this elongated watercourse into several sections. Of these a much reduced Torrens and a considerably larger Eyre are big enough to rank among

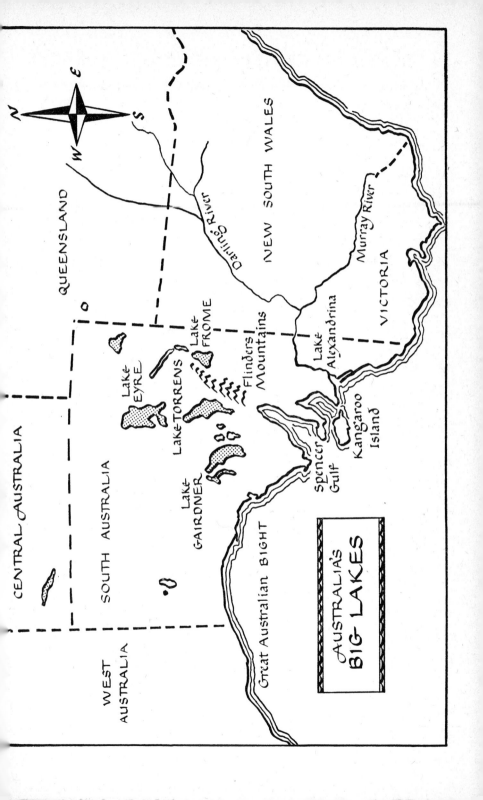

the world's great lakes. But whether they are lakes at all is doubtful, as we shall note presently.

Torrens, nearest the sea, is the most accessible. It was once a prolongation of Spencer Gulf, only thirty-five miles distant. A chain of shallow lakes or salt pans traces this connection, through which Upton and others reported a definite overflow. This must have been a transient phenomenon, for other observers have found little or no water in Torrens's dusty bed. At best it is a periodic lake or playa.

The shore lines are well defined, while the basin, 125 miles long by 30 broad, covers 2230 square miles. The surrounding scenery, particularly toward the north where much of the sandy terrain is crusted with salt, is described as "the most dreary imaginable."

The lake was named for Sir Robert Torrens, a member of the South Australian Land Commission and chairman of the Colonization Commission. Though his efforts to promote settlement in the interior were abortive, he is remembered for his improved method of registering land titles, a system adopted in certain districts in Europe, Canada, and the United States.

Early explorers in South Australia encountered almost insuperable difficulties. The aborigines knew every water hole or area where digging would yield enough soupy liquid to prevent death from thirst. Primitive children of the wilds, they devoured roots, grubs, and worms, while their keen vision could follow a lizard's trail invisible to white men. Like camels, they could traverse great distances with little or no water, then eat and drink prodigiously. Instances of this acquired capacity would stagger belief, were they not well authenticated. One native immediately downed three gallons of water with no ill effects; two others, over a six-hour period, consumed between them fifty pounds of kangaroo meat! White intruders into that dreary region had no such powers of adaptability. Moreover, the blacks, surly and suspicious, were an added peril, with their spears and whirring boomerangs, which seemed to defy the very laws of gravity. No wonder several early adventurers lost their lives, while all deserve the honor conferred upon them—Heroes of the Lonely Way.

One of the first of these explorers was Edward Eyre. In 1838 he set out for the interior but encountered an impassable obstacle in Torrens Lake. Much of its dry bed was black mud overlaid with salt crystals that gave off a blinding glare. Eyre, estimating the width at twenty miles, tried to cross on horseback. This proved impracticable, for in places he waded through water two feet deep, green as the sea, and quite as salt.

Farther north he came upon a similar and even larger basin which he assumed was a continuation of the first. Hence arose the myth of a super lake which befogged early geographers. Eyre did penetrate into the hinterland, but several of his horses perished, while beyond the horizon, so the natives informed him, stretched a limitless desert.

Efforts have been made to colonize districts west of Torrens. There the spinifex and other sparse vegetation is sometimes supplemented by grass following unusual rains, for the soil is fertile when water is obtainable. Herds of cattle and sheep have been driven there and isolated stations established. In 1922 E. T. Quayle reported that such settlements, by developing grasslands around Torrens and Lake Frome farther to the north, had arrested the encroachment of the desert and increased the rainfall! He even predicted a rise in lake levels. Unfortunately such optimism has withered during prolonged droughts, while most pioneers, disillusioned and bankrupt, have abandoned all attempts to subdue what remains an unconquered wilderness.

EYRE, THE "DEAD HEART OF THE CONTINENT"

More than a century ago, from a height called Mount Hope-less, Edward Eyre gazed out over salt-strewn flats to what he supposed were sheets of water shimmering in the distance. That vast playa or salt pan is now named for him, Lake Eyre.

Eyre is the largest and most intriguing of Australia's lake beds. Separated from Torrens to the south by forty miles of desert, nowhere more than five hundred feet high, it occupies the deepest portion of the Great Rift, here 39 feet below sea level. The lake bed is not only longer than Torrens, but considerably wider, in places approaching fifty miles. A bulging peninsula nearly divides it, the major section known as North Eyre, the lesser South Eyre. Together they exceed 3700 square miles, a larger area than Rudolf or Titicaca.

The vast drainage basin to the north is entirely shut off from the sea. Although its 450,000 square miles exceeds the drainage basin of all five of North America's Great Lakes, it supplies Eyre with little or no water. The considerable streams which meander toward it seldom arrive. The largest is Cooper Creek, upon whose banks those unhappy adventurers Bourke and Wills perished of starvation. Fed by the watershed of Queensland hundreds of miles away, its current disappears into the sand. The Warburton and Warriner, though also impressive upon a large-scale map, are little better than wadis flushed by periodic rains. For Eyre occupies the driest part of dry Australia, with an annual rainfall of only 4.1 inches.

The big lake has always been an enigma. No one ever sailed a boat upon its surface or measured its depth. In 1866 War-burton, exploring the northern sector, could find no water, only a "cracked and broken surface." In 1872–73 J. W. Lewis, mapping its shores, expressed his opinion when he wrote of Eyre, "I hope I may never see it again." From the highest marginal sand hills he failed to observe any water. Instead, the bottom, caked with salt three inches thick, was so nearly level that one member of his party, venturing seven miles from shore, found a declivity of only two and a half feet.

Professor Gregory, who named the Great African Rift, visited Eyre in the winter of 1902–03. Weird native tales about the bones of kadimakara monsters led him to investigate. These bones proved to be fossils of giant kangaroos and wombats long extinct. He concluded that the ocean had once swept down from the north to overflow all that region. Eyre, though far from the geographical midpoint, he called the "center of Australia." He also gave it another name little relished by patriotic countrymen: the "dead heart of the continent."

The lake was once several times its present area, but its shallow waters have retreated to expose a desert with little vegetation save clumps of spinifex.

The hazards of traversing such a country on horseback or even on camels long delayed exploration. But auto trucks equipped with balloon tires and still more serviceable airplanes have made Eyre better known. Halligan flew over it in 1922. From an elevation of 8000 feet he concluded that one third the lake bed was covered with water to an extreme depth of six fathoms. But when he returned with a boat he could find no water at all in Eyre or Torrens either.

A more systematic examination was made by C. T. Madigan in 1929. To be sure, a severe drought had persisted through the previous seven years, but the lake bed, as he flew across, presented only a pink expanse of gypsum crystals interspersed with white salt patches. Swooping low, he observed the tracks of animals, presumably camels seeking vainly for water! He let fall several spears with flags attached which remained erect, and, throwing overboard a box filled with sand, watched it burst while its contents scattered broadcast. He dared not land, for fear the plane might break through the crust and be unable to take off again, but he did skim the surface, raising a trail of dust. This uncanny plain was no lake, but the grave of one already dead.

Continuing his flight over Torrens and Frome, Madigan found no water anywhere. Not content, however, with so hurried an investigation, he returned to Eyre on a truck with inflated tires. Clearly marked beaches rose seventy feet above the lake bed. Across this nearly level floor he drove for fifty miles, not venturing far from the clay margin for fear of breaking through the saline crust. On this bed near the southern channel were the skeletons of seven camels that had perished of thirst. He spent a night in the vicinity, where he drilled holes to a depth of twenty feet. By morning water had risen in most of these holes to within a few inches of the surface; several had caved in, while one remained dry. The underlying water plane had subsided below the lake bottom.

Walking several miles straight out from shore, Madigan came upon more conclusive proofs, if proofs were needed. Around a dead needle bush were clustered the bones of fifteen rabbits. Still more decisive was a colony of black ants. Two thirds of the lake bottom seemed encrusted with salt and gypsum, but there was no water anywhere.

A later expedition conducted after a rainfall found moist earth at the mouths of several feeder creeks, but the lake bed remained as parched and dusty as before.

Against such evidence protests less convincing than emphatic have been urged in rebuttal. As recently as 1944 Morley Cutlack wrote, "I have seen hundreds of sea gulls around Lake Eyre." The inference was that aquatic birds knew water when they saw it, or was their inland quest a fruitless one?

Conflicting reports come from stock raisers from the wide-open spaces to the west. Lured into the wilderness by rains which produce adequate pasturage every ten or twelve years, they have been starved out by dreary intervals of drought. Few of them probably visited the Eyre beaches more than once a year, if that often. Most of them observed only a vacant expanse, but some thought they could detect shallow waters in the distance. In the blistering heat, however, the range of visibility seldom exceeds two miles.

The conclusion seems inescapable. The bed of this once great lake contains, at most, a modicum of moisture following seasons of uncommon rainfall. The distant waters glimpsed by occasional observers were probably heat waves refracted from fields of salt and gypsum. Lake Eyre is little more than a mirage.

GAIRDNER, A SALINE MUD FLAT

The huge Torrens horseshoe which Edward Eyre estimated to be four hundred miles in length was nearer six hundred. But later surveys have broken it up into sections, including not only the present Torrens and still larger Eyre, but also Gregory, Blanche, Callabonna, and Frome, as well as several lesser depressions. These loop about the Flinders Mountains, which rose as the surrounding Rift subsided.

Farther to the west lies another cluster of so-called lakes including Everard, Harris, Acraman, and Labyrinth. The largest is Gairdner, less extensive than Torrens but quite 100 miles long by perhaps 25 broad. Discounting numerous islets, or rather hillocks, above its dry bed, it somewhat exceeds our minimum of 1500 square miles, though at best it is only a playa or periodic lake.

Gairdner is about a hundred miles west of Torrens and extends even farther to the south, where the low Gawler range separates it from the sea. The Stuart Mountains shut off Lake Eyre, but to the eastward several lesser lake beds, including Macfarlane, Birthday, Island, and others connect it with the Torrens basin.

Gairdner was discovered in 1857 by Stephen Hart, who led an expedition inland from Streaky Bay on the seacoast. Approaching its western shore, he reported it a pastoral country. Later visitors dismissed the big lake as a "saline mud flat ninety miles long, of no economic importance."

In spite of Hart's early optimism, much of the surrounding country remains desolate and relatively inaccessible. Early voyagers along the "bight" were repelled by a coast so bleak and inhospitable. William Dampier called the aborigines "the miserablest people on earth." True, the native black is a primitive human, less intelligent than the Cro-Magnon cave dwellers of the European Stone Age. Retarded by his environment, he has made little progress during thousands of years, for his extreme antiquity is disclosed by the discovery of stone hatchets in marine clays fifteen feet below sea level. In spite of his jet skin, he has been identified as a degenerate member of the white race, while his nearest living relatives are the Veddahs of Ceylon and certain Dravidian tribes of the Hindu Deccan. Morose and sometimes hostile, his suspicions have been justified, for early settlers sought to destroy him like a dangerous animal.

These settlers also found a strange wild life. For Old Man Kangaroo they developed wholesome respect, for with one stroke of his powerful hind leg he could rip open a dog. He had even been known to drown a man by deliberately holding him under water. Such perils, however, were minor incidents compared with the aridity and scorching heat. One explorer reported the "ground heated to a depth of three feet, while

the horn handles of native knives split into long slivers."
Even settled regions wilted before hot blasts that swept from
the interior as from an opened furnace door. To quote an
observer, "Horses stood with drooped heads without energy
to lift them, birds sat perched, voiceless and openmouthed—
while a thermometer applied to the surface of the ground
registered 160 degrees."

Excessive dryness was a still greater barrier. Waterless
stretches of six hundred miles have been reported. Across one
such burning waste camels struggled for thirteen days without
a drink, while the thermometer daily soared above a hundred
degrees in the shade. No wonder the aborigines learned to
extract moisture from roots or, unearthing a living frog from
the caked earth, squeezed a little water from his body.

This barren hinterland is a family skeleton to the Australian.
He prefers to ignore it, minimize its importance, and enlarge
upon the prospects of more favored regions. Patriotism rebels
at accepting dead or dying lakes as a token of his country's
restricted future.

Central Australia, though largely barren, has a number of
lakes, while they dot that vast area known as West Australia.
Some doubtless contain far more water than Torrens or Eyre
or Gairdner. But those three vacant basins in the Australian
Rift are the only ones whose areas warrant inclusion among
the world's big lakes.

VII

European Lakes

ICE-LOCKED LADOGA

The huge icecap which once buried northern Europe vanished long ago. But scattered through Finland and the neighboring Russian terrain are thousands of lakes gouged out by this restless ocean of ice and filled with the melted residue.

Most impressive of these is Ladoga, the largest lake in Europe. Its area is almost exactly 7000 square miles, slightly smaller than the state of New Jersey or Lake Ontario. As it lies in that indefinite borderland between Russia and Finland, the expanding Soviet Empire has recently engulfed the big lake, together with some adjacent territory.

Ladoga is rather compact. Its outline, while neither oval nor oblong, suggests something of both. The major axis slants a little west of north for 125 miles, while its width is more than half as great. With the exception of the extreme southern edge, it extends beyond the 60th parallel, or roughly the latitude of Great Slave Lake in Canada.

Ladoga's maximum depth—730 feet—dips far below sea level as its altitude is only 55 feet. Dense fogs veil its surface, while fierce Arctic gales seem to produce movements in the waters not unlike the currents of the ocean. They flow from north to south along the western shores to rotate endlessly. Great tremors also agitate the surface, the familiar seiches of Alpine lakes, caused, it is believed, by disturbances in atmospheric pressure. Though distinct from marine tides, they are not incomparable, as they sometimes raise the prevalent level seven feet or more.

This great relic of the Ice Age annually reverts to type, remaining frozen from October until March. The surface congeals to a depth of three feet or more, while winter storms sometimes drive one sheet of ice above another until jagged ramparts seventy or eighty feet high pile up along the leeward shore. In the spring the waters reappear clear and blue but decidedly cold, for the surface temperature hovers near the freezing mark until late in summer, when it may rise to 53 degrees.

The lake empties into the Gulf of Finland through the short Neva River. It is a natural refrigerator to Leningrad, the city that Peter the Great erected upon stakes driven into the marshes as a window opening upon Europe. In this city the tsars maintained their seat of government and their famous Winter Palace was well named. For even in June the big lake gives the city a second taste of winter when the Neva becomes clogged with drifting ice.

In fact Ladoga is icebound more than half the time. Navigation over its treacherous surface is confined to 180 days a year, when steamers resume their busy trade routes. Fishing is also important, but most small boats avoid the open waters because of sudden storms. For their accommodation a network of canals crisscrosses the neighboring lowlands, connecting with the seventy streams that empty into the lake.

Like Baikal, Ladoga has its seals and its marine crustaceans, distinctly Arctic in origin. Hence geologists suspect there was once a direct communication with that frigid sea now barred by the dreary lake region toward the north and the interminable spruce forests of Finland.

ONEGA AND ITS CANALS

To the east and somewhat to the north of Ladoga lies Onega, the second in point of size among Russia's big lakes. It is even longer than Ladoga, 145 miles, but has little more than half the latter's area, or 3764 square miles. This is somewhat larger than those other members of the world's great lakes—Rudolf, Nicaragua, and Titicaca.

Onega's main axis slants from southeast to northwest, the direction of the glacial drift, as the continental icecap retreated. The southern shore line is fairly uniform, with a maximum width of forty-five miles, but the northern is indented by sinuous bays and dotted with islands, while numerous submerged rocks add a peril to navigation. Here the lake approaches within less than a hundred miles of the White Sea, suggesting a former connection shut off by a slowly rising terrain. Instead the big lake discharges into Ladoga through the Svir River, to add its remarkably pure overflow to the ever freshening Baltic.

The coast line is predominantly low, as the loftiest neighboring altitude is but 160 feet. It is fairly well settled also, with the development of timber cutting, mining, and fishing. Great rafts of logs, like moving islands, drift over its surface in summer, and lake steamers, introduced as far back as 1832, move to and fro among fleets of fishing boats. Salmon and lake trout are commercially the most valuable fish. Commerce is encouraged by a series of canals which launch out from the Svir River to connect with a branch of the Volga, Russia's great inland waterway.

The railway to the ice-free Murmansk coast, the Soviet's only unimpeded outlet to the Atlantic, runs close to Onega's

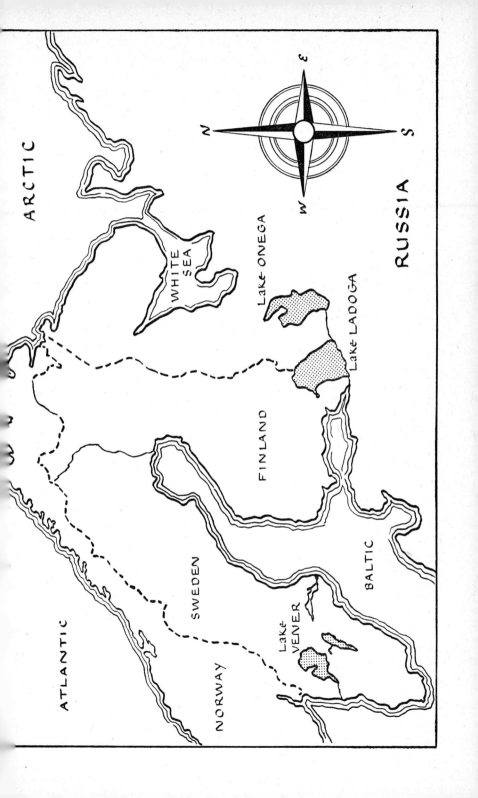

western shore line, which has undergone a notable development in consequence.

Ice is less of a problem than in Ladoga, whose more spacious surface permits unmelted sheets to drift about until late spring. Navigation on Onega begins about the middle of May and continues well into December, for an average duration of 209 days.

Several rivers drain into the lake, so that seasonal thaws raise water levels two feet or more. The greatest depth seems to be 408 feet, although statistics on the subject are incomplete and contradictory.

Among the elaborate plans of Soviet management is the development of Onega as a trade center. An approach by canal to the White Sea offers no insuperable engineering problem. Such a project would place the lake in the center of intricate waterways linking three widely separated seas: the Arctic, the Baltic, and the Caspian. But this is a foray into the future, when even the geography of our friendly lakes may be revised to order.

BEAUTIFUL VENER

The third member of Europe's big lakes, situated in southern Sweden, is variously spelled Vener and Vanern. Though the smallest of the three, with an area of 2149 square miles, it is far the most beautiful, in a region noted for its wild and rugged terrain. The northern shores are rocky and in the main densely forested; the southern lower, more settled, and offering many delightful vistas. Among the numerous islands, Lecko in particular is admired for the ancient castle which lends it a medieval glamor.

The major axis of the lake extends some 87 miles from southwest to northeast, while the greatest width is about 44.

The deepest recorded sounding is 292 feet. Rocky peninsulas and islands divide the waters into two sections, the smaller lying to the southwest, locally known as Lake Dalbo.

Numerous tributaries maintain the clear cold waters from a drainage basin of 18,720 square miles. The largest of these tributaries, the Klar River, bears rains and melted snows from the northland. Hence in the rainy season lake levels may rise ten feet or more.

Fish abound and fishing craft add a picturesque touch to the numerous more pretentious trading vessels that ply the surface. For Vener is a busy highway of commerce. From rich deposits to the north come cargoes of iron ore; timber is an important item, as are agricultural and dairy products and a wide variety of manufactured articles. Commercial activity has been enhanced by a canal connecting with Fredrikshald in Norway, while another supplements the Göta River as an outlet to the Kattegat. A number of busy ports and manufacturing towns have sprung up along the shores, so that Vener suggests a miniature edition of North America's Great Lakes. Glacial action is everywhere apparent in rounded boulders, deep scratches etched on outcroppings, and numerous moraines. The lake itself is a greater memento of the continental icecap which buried the region not many thousands of years ago. In that frigid era the shallow Baltic was only a gigantic icebox which slowly filled with glacial meltings to become a huge fresh-water lake called by geologists Ancylus. Even now the Gulf of Bothnia is the freshest of all seas, with only about one fifth the saline content of the outer Atlantic. As the ice disappeared and the ocean reoccupied its ancient boundaries, Vener seems to have been a gulf of the sea which still approaches within less than twenty-five miles through one of its numerous fiords. Evidence of this union persists in degenerate types of marine fauna which survive in Vener's fresh waters.

At Sjötorp, the terminus of the Göta Canal, lake levels have been recorded for well over a century. From such data Dr. Wallon has projected three periods, one of two to three years, a second of about eleven, and a third of forty. These shed light on variations which seem to follow definite cycles. The science of limnology, however, still in its infancy, can offer only fragmentary hints on the rise and fall of subterranean water planes as they are thus revealed.

VIII

North American Lakes

THE CANADIAN SHIELD

Across two million square miles of North American terrain
sprawls the great Canadian or Laurentian Shield. It was a
worn-out continent even before pre-Cambrian times, five hundred million years ago! Its rocks, among the oldest known,
expose the surface of a different, younger world when most
of the Western Hemisphere lay beneath the sea and life was
just emerging from the primeval slime. Yet they still drip with
the meltings of the enormous icecap, thousands of feet in
thickness, that once overspread the region, an excess of moisture that persists in ill-assorted rivers and almost innumerable
lakes. On the threshold of this desolate landscape one seems
like an intruder in the workshop of creation before the master
design has taken shape out of chaos, such is the confusion of
almost formless waters amid smoothly rounded hills and a
maze of interminable muskegs and moraines.

Although the Shield properly includes the Adirondacks and
some of the Appalachian ranges, it culminates in those bleak
tablelands of Labrador which loom seven thousand feet above
Hudson Strait. In the southern sector immense forests, particularly of spruce, clothe its nakedness, but in those drearier
districts pre-empted by the musk ox and the caribou the green
nap of vegetation is worn threadbare in the great barren
ground. This merges into that archipelago of more than 500,-
000 square miles which extends for 1300 miles east and west by

1500 north and south. In area it is the only island group that can remotely challenge the East Indies, but there all likeness ends, for against the latter's tropic fertility it lays bare a waste of wind-swept ledges and frozen tundra interspersed with accumulations of never melting ice.

Of the Shield, Coleman writes, "Canada combines the largest area of very ancient pre-Cambrian rocks with the most youthful arrangement of rivers to be found in any continent. . . . The number of lakes and waterfalls probably exceeds that of the rest of the world."

Certainly no geographer has ever tried to count all the lakes on the Canadian Shield. Many have no names, have never even been sighted by white men save in fleeting glimpses from airplanes. Some are very large, covering hundreds of square miles. Two, at least, Dubawnt and Reindeer, are among the world's major bodies of fresh water. Others, even more imposing, like Great Bear and Great Slave lakes, lie partly within the Shield itself, partly along the border of that vast continental plain stretching westward to the Rockies, where three great rivers drain the saturated landscape—the St. Lawrence, the Saskatchewan, and the Mackenzie.

The Canadian Shield holds fabulous mineral wealth. It is one of Nature's major storehouses of gold, silver, copper, nickel, cobalt, lead, zinc, and those rarer elements uranium and radium. Here also are enormous untapped resources of timber and water power.

Historically, the Shield has proved a formidable barrier to the advance of civilization. Would-be settlers have outflanked it rather than attempt a frontal assault. Few have ventured into its innermost recesses, save those hardy souls who are ready to dare anything for furs or minerals.

Glacial action stripped off much of its soil and disorganized or obliterated older river systems. Every large-scale map reveals a veritable rash of lakes which almost overlap one another, spilling out their contents until rivers become mere swollen chains. Although many lakes elsewhere have no outlet, some of these have two or more, discharging through divergent rivers into widely separated seas. Loneliness and emptiness brood over a land that, with all its abounding waters, is more sparsely populated than the Sahara.

No wonder explorers have called this forbidding region "a wilderness of rock and spruce with lakes literally by the million." That number is exaggerated, yet the famous Lake District of England, beloved of the poet Wordsworth and his school, could be tucked away and forgotten in any one of a hundred nooks and crannies of the great Canadian Shield.

THE GREAT LAKES

Pre-eminent above all others are those vast fresh-water seas along the southern Canadian border which are universally recognized as the *Great* Lakes. From Duluth, at the farthest extremity of Superior, to Ontario's outlet among the forested islands of the St. Lawrence they stretch for 1160 miles, a watery surface of 96,000 square miles in a drainage basin of 300,000.

Their geological origin is of interest not only in itself, but because it tells us something of the life history of many lesser lakes. Millions of years ago the entire region lay beneath a shallow sea. Upon its submerged floor the sweepings of the uplands settled in a layer of shale and sandstone perhaps three hundred feet in thickness. Over this layer spread successive carpets of calcareous ooze—the remains of countless living organisms—which were compressed into a second layer formed of limestone ranging in thickness from a hundred and fifty to two hundred feet. Above this stratum—which was tougher

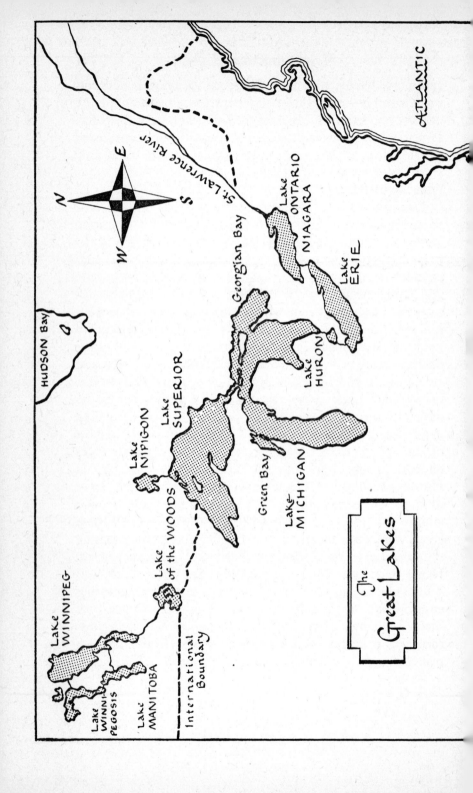

The Great Lakes

and more durable than most limestone—additional sediments solidified in a third layer of softer marl to a maximum depth of three hundred feet. Much of the latter, known as the Salina formation, was heavily impregnated with salt. All this occurred in the Paleozoic Age to complete the *structural* foundation from which were carved the beds of the Great Lakes as we know them today.

Then came a second stage—the era of *emergence*. A slow upheaval of the global crust elevated the region two thousand feet or more above the sea. How many ages passed before this part of the continent rose dripping out of the ocean is conjectural, but it was a long, long time as measured by more familiar calendars. It was followed, and, in fact, accompanied by, a third stage, the era of *erosion*, for those agents of destruction—the winds, the rains, and the frosts—labor tirelessly to reduce all elevations to the dead flatness of sea level. During this period the beds of the Great Lakes became the valleys of rivers now unknown, which probably differed little from that of the Ohio River today. But this vast abrasion was by no means uniform, and underlying rock strata varied in both depth and extent. Hence the beds of Lake Erie, as well as most of Huron and Michigan, were excavated from the upper layer of marl; while Green Bay in Michigan, Georgian Bay in Huron, and much of Ontario cut through the second layer of limestone to the shales and sandstones underneath. Erosion gouged still deeper in the basin of Superior, where all three layers were worn away in a vast bowllike depression, exposing the older, harder rocks that formed the floor of the ancient sea. Hence Superior is much the deepest of the Great Lakes.

So much for the essential groundwork. Further sculpturing ensued during the glacial era, from the grinding of great ice sheets, the plowing up of terminal moraines, and further disturbances in global surface levels. For the Great Lakes are really gigantic mementos of that continent of ice that once spread south of the Ohio River to bury four million square miles of North America.

This frigid covering advanced and retreated over long intervals as the world climate was slowly stabilized, then haltingly withdrew to Greenland and adjacent islands, where it still defies lengthening summer thaws.

As the icecap melted, huge lakes seeped out along the southern edge to carve beaches at much higher levels and remote from present shores. One of these lakes, called Chicago, embraced the southern section of Lake Michigan and overflowed into the Mississippi. Another, Lake Duluth, filled the western extremity of Superior where, shut off from northern outlets by the impassable ice barrier, it also drained into the Mississippi.

Traces of these prehistoric waters abound most in regions east of Michigan. Lake Maumee accumulated about the southern arc of Huron to include much of Erie also. Later Lake Arkona overspread all of Erie—first of the five Great Lakes to be emancipated from the ice, extending far beyond present shore lines to be engulfed in turn by still larger Lake Whittlesey. As the ice retreated into Canada an enormous new lake, Algonquin, swallowed up Superior, Michigan, and Huron, with much adjacent territory, leaving beaches 435 feet above Huron's present level. It flowed eastward but avoided the circuitous Niagara route. Other lakes appeared, such as Iroquois, which drained into the Hudson and eventually dwindled to the present shore lines of Ontario.

Then the map becomes more jumbled and confused. Terminal moraines were heaped up along the edges of these fluctuating lakes to alter both shore lines and outlets. As order emerged from chaos the trend was eastward, but an almost imperceptible westward tilting of surface strata amounting to only three inches in the mile would have diverted four of the Great Lakes to the Mississippi, left Niagara a beetling cliff, and reduced the St. Lawrence to relative unimportance.

Even now the Great Lake terrain is thought to be slowly shifting, rising in the north and subsiding in the south at a rate estimated to be about five inches to the hundred miles per century.

Geographers have marveled at how the Great Lakes maintain themselves in a drainage area so restricted in contrast with their imposing dimensions. Meteorologists are studying the problem, but the water supply seems adequate, fed by an annual precipitation which ranges from 27 inches over Superior to 34 over Ontario. Much of this rainfall evaporates, yet it overflows through the St. Clair River at the rate of 175,000 cubic feet per second; 192,000 through the Niagara River, and 229,000 from Ontario into the St. Lawrence.

The history of the Great Lakes assumes vague outlines from native tradition. Particularly venerated was the northern shore of Superior, known as Gitche Gumee—the big sea water—with its capacious bays and bold promontories. Most impressive of these was Thunder Cape, a Gibraltar-like ridge of basaltic rock several miles long and 1300 feet high, guarding the entrance to cavernous Thunder Bay. In the jagged sky line of this ridge the Indians beheld the recumbent form of the Great Spirit and listened awe-struck as his voice reverberated from the heights in storms. Near the cleft, through which the Nipigon pours its icy waters, towers the famous Red Rock where they quarried their peace pipes or calumets. Lake Huron also had its local shrine in White Rock, while other prominent landscape features were equally revered.

Unfortunately, smoking the peace pipe was but an infrequent interlude in bloody warfare. Both the Eries and the Hurons, whose names survive in two of the Great Lakes, were all but exterminated by the Iroquois. These Indians, more settled than most, built commodious lodges in what is now New York State, cultivated maize, squashes, sunflowers, and other vegetables and herbs, and developed a crude government, the

Confederacy of the Five, later Six, Nations. Asserting an arrogant superiority over their neighbors, they were aggressive warriors whose courage was too often marred by acts of fiendish cruelty. Though never numerous, they sent raiding parties as far west as the Mississippi, as far south as the Gulf of Mexico. By the year 1643 they had obtained from unscrupulous Dutch traders on the Hudson four hundred guns, which gave them a decisive advantage over opponents armed with lances and flint-headed arrows.

Indian warfare played a somber role in European colonization. The French, who were the first white men to explore the Great Lakes, were more adept at winning the good will of native tribes than were either the English or colonials. But unfortunately for their dreams of empire, they aroused the undying enmity of the Iroquois. That knightly adventurer, Samuel de Champlain, while exploring the beautiful lake that bears his name, aided his little band of Canadian Indians in a scrimmage with the Mohawks, most ferocious of the Five Nations, an affront which the latter never forgave. This incident, though seemingly trivial, had far-reaching consequences, for the fury of the Iroquois not only diverted French explorations northward and delayed the discovery of Lake Erie, but proved a check upon the expansion of the French dominions in the New World.

Indians navigated the Great Lakes in birch-bark canoes. They hugged the shores for refuge from sudden storms, reckoned distances as "so many days' journey," and even sketched maps on bark or skins. The island of Michilimackinac was a favorite rendezvous for Ojibway, Huron, and Ottawa fishermen, who were so adept that white men had little to teach their dusky-skinned brothers. They also mined copper from the rich deposits on the shores of Lake Superior and even carried on a considerable commerce. The Ottawa Indians on the island of Grand Manitoulin in Huron were particularly enterprising.

Their copper implements and adornments, furs, tobacco, sun-flower oil, herbs, and other commodities passed from hand to hand in barter to markets fifteen hundred miles away.

The first European to hear of the Great Lakes was Jacques Cartier on his second voyage to America in 1535. Forced to seek harborage over against the big island of Anticosti on the feast day of St. Lawrence, he gave that name to the surrounding waters. He knew little of the immense bay, still less of the noble river beyond. The Indians informed him that this river "was without end," but the Breton sea saptain proceeded until stopped by the foaming Lachine Rapids. Climbing Mount Réal, in the heart of what is now the great city of Montreal, he gazed westward where the broad channels lose themselves among wooded islands. He was told of "a fresh-water sea of which there is no mention of anyone having seen the bounds" which may have been Ontario, but more probably Huron, nor did he doubt that the great river at his feet presented a new route to the East Indies.

Champlain, governor of Canada, who in 1609 founded the city of Quebec, heard more definite reports of enormous bodies of water in the wilderness. Of Huron he wrote, "Without doubt this can be nothing else than the South Sea," for some Indian accounts implied that its waters were salt. Champlain realized, however, that to traverse the forests that intervened a European must master the language of the natives and adopt their customs. So he encouraged youthful Frenchmen, ambitious to serve king and country, to pioneer in exploring the unknown hinterland.

Of these adventurers the most illustrious was Etienne Brulé. In 1612, perhaps even earlier, he accompanied a group of Hurons to their winter quarters on the shores of Georgian Bay: probably the first white man to sight any one of the Great Lakes. Thither, three years later, Champlain followed in person, and wrote of the lake, "It is so vast that they [the

Indians] will not put out into the same for fear lest some storm or gale may surprise them."

That same year, 1615, Brulé, with a party of twelve natives, reached the shore of Ontario, near where the city of Toronto now stands. His explorations in Superior, however, are less readily substantiated. Of this lake he wrote, "Beyond the Sweetwater Sea [Huron] there is another very large lake— the said lake and the Sweetwater Sea extend together for thirty days journey by canoe according to the Indian accounts." In 1622, with a French companion, Grenolle, he seems to have navigated his canoes along the southern coast of Superior to the copper country, bringing back copper implements as evidence. It is also possible, if not indeed probable, that he may have sighted Lake Erie on his excursion to the so-called Neutral Ground in 1624. Explorers long shunned that dangerous territory from fear of the Iroquois, so that it was not until 1640 that the Jesuit missionaries, Brébeuf and Chaumonot, recounted their visit to its shores.

Meanwhile Brulé had followed Indian trails southward to Chesapeake Bay. Returning, he blundered, half starved, into a village of the Senecas. These bloodthirsty Iroquois, recognizing him as a hated Frenchman, tore out his fingernails with their teeth, plucked out the hairs of his beard one by one, burned his body with red-hot brands, and were proceeding to execute him by slow torture when a thunderstorm which burst as if in answer to his invocation so impressed the superstitious savages that they conducted him in safety to the border of the friendly Huron country.

Perhaps Brulé had other sensational adventures, lost to the world for want of a chronicler. His death at the age of forty was a lurid terminus to his eventful life. Grown dissolute from his savage associates, he was murdered by members of the Bear Clan of the Hurons, who ate a portion of his remains to acquire something of his strength and courage. This revolting tragedy cut short a career unparalleled in the history of Great Lake discoveries. Champlain, however, suspecting that his one-time protégé had conducted treasonable negotiations with the English, did not avenge his death.

Based upon the reports of Brulé and others that followed in his footsteps, Champlain, in 1632, sketched the first European map of the Great Lakes. This map showed but three of them: Grand Lac (Superior), Lac St. Louis (Ontario), and "Mer Douce," the fresh-water sea of Huron. If Brulé had told him of Erie, Champlain ignored the report, while of Lake Michigan he as yet knew nothing. For that fifth member of the five Great Lakes was discovered two years later by another French enthusiast, Jean Nicolet, who, like Brulé, had become both interpreter and seeker after far places for Champlain.

In 1634 Nicolet might have been observed coasting the northern shore line of Lake Michigan in a huge canoe paddled by seven stout Hurons, bearing with him an embroidered robe "of China damask, all strewn with flowers and birds of many colors," to wear when interviewing the emperor of China. Entering Green Bay and proceeding to its farthest extremity, he encountered the fabled "men of the sea" who were not, as he had dreamed, vassals of a Mongolian despot but simple Winnebago Indians. Not long after this adventure Nicolet was drowned in the St. Lawrence when a sudden storm swamped his canoe.

The first European vessels to usher in the grand drama of navigation on the Great Lakes were four tiny "barks" of ten tons burden, built, according to Father Hennepin, by the Sieur de la Salle at Fort Frontenac, now Kingston, on Ontario. Passage westward, however, was barred by Niagara, first described by the Jesuit Ragueneau in 1647 as "a waterfall of dreadful height." By-passing the falls, which Father Hennepin estimated were 600 feet high, La Salle paused some miles beyond to set his ship carpenters at work felling trees and fashioning planks and timbers for a stout craft which he named the *Griffon*. As she was to venture into perilous regions, he equipped her with five small cannon and two arquebuses. She made a brave appearance when she set sail on Lake Erie August 7, 1679, with pennons fluttering from her two masts and her sails billowing in the breeze. Delayed in Huron by a storm, she entered Lake Michigan in September and proceeded to Green Bay, where La Salle, fortunately for him, left to explore the Mississippi. There she took on a cargo of furs. On this voyage the Danish pilot, according to Father Hennepin, "did nothing . . . but curse and swear against M. de la Salle who had brought him thither to make him perish in a nasty lake." His profane prophecy was justified by the event, for on her return voyage the little vessel foundered with all on board, the first of many shipwrecks in these dangerous waters.

European commerce on the Great Lakes was long confined to furs and trade goods. Later salt became an important commodity. The earliest shipment of wheat seems to have been made in 1838. The *Eureka*, which cleared from Cleveland in 1849 bound for the California gold fields, not only gave an impetus to passenger service but forecast the linking of these vast inland waterways with the oceans.

Cuthbertson remarks, "In four hundred years the Great Lake basin has changed from an unknown wilderness to the most crowded waterway in the world"; how crowded may be inferred from the statistics of that prosperous year 1929 when the commerce of the Great Lakes totaled 297,182,061 tons valued at $4,294,385,683. These astronomical figures acquire more meaning when we learn that they fell only 10 per cent under freight receipts and shipments from all the seaports of the United States on the Atlantic, the Gulf of Mexico, and the Pacific combined. Louis Jolliet, the first European to descend the Detroit River, would rub his eyes today, for it probably carries more traffic than any other river, canal, or ocean strait in the world.

Winter clamps icy fetters upon this activity. Like Russia, the Great Lakes long for an ice-free port. Superior usually freezes on December 9, to remain deserted until April 12; Michigan follows suit from December 15 until April 12; Huron renews the silence of Algonquin days from December 17 until April 6; Ontario from December 18 to April 5, and Erie, farther southward, takes a prolonged holiday from December 17 to March 30.

While it is doubtful whether the average winter freezes more than a third of the water surface of the Great Lakes, the major ports are sealed by sheets of ice driven shoreward by winter gales and piled layer upon layer to an extreme height of fifty feet or more.

Each lake is subject to curious movements and oscillations that tend to circumvent the frost. First is the steady current sweeping onward toward the St. Lawrence. True, average tides are almost imperceptible—little over an inch—but spring tides may show a range of three inches, and Superior reports tides of eight inches or more. Seiches, mainly due to barometric disturbances, are more noticeable. In Lake Michigan nine seiches within twenty-four hours have been observed following the longer axis with more frequent transverse movements. Currents also follow a counterclockwise direction as revealed by bottle floats. Some miles off the port of Cleveland a current sets eastward at the rate of four miles per hour.

Winds are a more disturbing factor. In shallow Erie storms of near hurricane velocity have heaped the waters along one extremity of the lake more than seven feet higher than normal, with a proportionate lowering elsewhere. On April 7, 1893, the water level at Chicago rose five feet.

The Great Lakes are as accurately charted and well lighted as any part of the seacoast. The most isolated lighthouse in America is not on some Atlantic shoal but on Stannard Rock in Superior, twenty-four miles from the nearest land. For the

Great Lakes, when lashed by storms, become more perilous than the ocean. There skilled navigators seek an "offing" and "lay to" until calmer weather. But no such elbow room is possible on the Great Lakes. From any direction a lee shore may suddenly loom up beyond seething breakers. So it is just as well that traffic is forced to suspend in winter, when snow squalls and shrieking gales would multiply the risks of shipwreck.

The deep passageways that lead from lake to lake show little tendency to silt up. Yet great dredges furrow them anew from time to time, while hundreds of millions of dollars have been expended in docks, breakwaters, and harbor approaches. The Erie Canal, opened in 1825, first gave direct access to the undeveloped hinterland and established the port of New York as the major outlet to the Old World. The Welland Canal, by an elaborate series of locks, raised and lowered shipping past Niagara's formidable barrier, insuring access to the sea. More controversial is the sanitation and ship canal at Chicago. That city, as a war measure, was permitted by the government to withdraw 8500 cubic feet a minute from Lake Michigan for sewage disposal. Through this canal boats of shallow draft may proceed to the Mississippi, along the route once followed by the spillway of the Ice Age. Such integrating of the Great Lakes with the Mississippi Valley has been condemned by other ports, which fear that lowering lake levels may endanger their harbor approaches. Still more ambitious is the proposed ship canal, which would offer easier communication between the Great Lakes and the Atlantic via the St. Lawrence. This project, whose cost would rocket into the hundreds of millions, has been thrust into the background, but remains a live issue in the development of Great Lake resources.

Shores whose solitudes were once disturbed only by Indian encampments now boast flourishing cities. Toronto is the metropolis of Ontario; Lake Erie, among lesser communities, has two major cities in Cleveland and Buffalo; Huron has no great port, but Detroit, overlooking the narrow outlet, has become a world center. Michigan has Milwaukee and Chicago of amazing growth; while Duluth on Superior, though not in the same census classification, has become the greatest iron port in the world and in shipping tonnage is outranked only by New York among the nation's ports. The eight states and one Canadian province that border the five Great Lakes have changed from a wilderness inhabited by a few thousand warring savages to an empire with a population of 45,000,000.

Although their usefulness as highways of commerce eclipses other values, the Great Lakes have fabulous resources. Nearby areas show rich mineral deposits. The forests that once echoed to the war cries of Hurons and Ojibways produce an annual fortune in lumber and pulp wood; manufacturing interests are varied and well-nigh numberless; fishing, particularly for the salmon, trout, lake whitefish, and the giant muskellunge, has its romantic setting; while the cities along their banks enjoy an unfailing water supply. New York, whose reservoirs in distant hills sometimes necessitate rationing, and when completed will require an estimated $800,000,000; or Los Angeles, whose aqueduct to the Colorado River is 392 miles long, leads through 92 miles of tunnels, and cost $220,000,000, may well envy Cleveland its Lake Erie, or Chicago its Michigan. In fact the surplus overflow through the St. Lawrence, now lost in the Atlantic, would meet the requirements of the entire United States.

The recent transformation of water power into electricity is a modern miracle. Niagara, harnessed to gigantic dynamos, now transmits such power two hundred miles or more by high-tension wires. Thirty-six thousand cubic feet of water per second is diverted from the Canadian Falls, and 20,000 from the American, a lessening of volume which does not seriously impair the grandeur of the spectacle. Surely no vision invoked by the incantations of an Iroquois medicine man ever rivaled such wizardry as this. Nor has the final word been written. Still greater achievements are in store when the two nations most concerned recognize more fully the unequaled advantages which are theirs in the grandest lakes on earth.

SUPERIOR

The Great Lakes are too well known to require more than a few sketchy highlights, but their immense importance demands separate treatment.

Champlain knew Superior as Grand Lac, but on the Jesuit map of 1672 it appears as Lac Supérieur. This merely fixed its position "above" or "beyond" better-known Lake Huron, but the English derivative was so felicitous that it has been retained. This inland sea is indeed superior—the finest body of fresh water in the world.

To be sure, Baikal in Asia, relatively narrow but incredibly deep, has a greater volume, while those vast African troughs, Lakes Tanganyika and Nyasa, may prove rivals in content. But the observer is no more impressed by depths of four thousand feet than four hundred, while the eye that peers in vain for an opposite shore is overwhelmed by illimitable horizons. Superior's length in a right line is 350 miles—the "steamer track" 383—the extreme width 160. Its rugged coast line is 2100 miles long. Its area, 31,820 square miles, tops that of Victoria Nyanza, its closest rival, by more than five thousand. Only that section of recaptured ocean, the Caspian, outranks it among inland waters, and the Caspian is salt.

Moreover, Superior is deep. The United States Lake Survey records a maximum of 1290 feet, while the Hydrographic and Map Service of Ottawa notes an abyss fourteen miles off Caribou Island Light where 1302 feet was indicated. Although Superior's elevation is 602 feet, much of its submerged floor lies far below sea level. Its average depth is 487 feet, its volume of water 2927 cubic miles. This would flood New England to a depth of over two hundred feet. Superior is capacious enough to swallow all four of the other Great Lakes with an additional Ontario for good measure.

Over Superior's drainage basin of 80,900 square miles, the annual rainfall is 27 inches. Among its many affluents the largest is the Nipigon River, whose sparkling waters come tumbling down from the big lake of that name among the northern highlands.

Superior has been called the most oceanic of lakes. The great combers that smash against its northern Iron Coast suggest the ocean front of Oregon or Maine. There are deep gulfs —Thunder Bay, Black Bay, and Nipigon—outlined by cliffs hundreds of feet high and flanked by majestic headlands, for here the Canadian Shield intrudes in such commanding heights as Thunder Cape and Gargantua Head. No wonder the primitive red man, when he viewed this bold escarpment, felt himself in the very presence of the Great Spirit.

That restless adventurer Brulé and his companion Grenolle were probably the first white men to visit Superior. The year was 1622. Pierre Radisson and his half brother-in-law, Groseilliers, known to the English as "Gooseberry," followed in 1659–60. Setting out from Montreal with several Indian companions, they made Georgian Bay on Huron in the fast time of twenty-two days. There was urgent cause for haste—the menace of hostile tribes to the south. In Radisson's picturesque language, "We left the Iroquois in his fort and the feare in our breeches" and "rowed from Friday to Tuesday without intermission." On the south shore of Superior they traded with natives who were in "hopes to gett knives from us which they love better than we serve God." The little party also skirted some of the northern shore, and in the western sector traded with the Sioux Indians, whom he called "the nation of the beefe," from their use of bison meat and hides. He described the shore line in misspelled English for the edification of Charles II, and portrayed the life of the explorer in such colorful phrases as "the feare in the buttocks, to have the belly empty, the weariness of the bones." Radisson returned, his canoes laden with beaver skins, only to have them confiscated by the French governor. This highhanded act led to his desertion to the English and the founding of the Hudson's Bay Company.

Other Frenchmen followed the western trail. Daniel Greysolon, the Sieur Du Lhut in 1679, explored the country to the west, bought fifty canoeloads of furs, and by his courtesy and justice won the respect of warring tribes. His trading post is remembered in the English corruption of his name, Duluth. Pierre la Vérendrye also visited Superior in 1731.

Several islands break the vast expanse. Of these Isle Royale, 44 miles long by 15 broad, is at once the most considerable and the most intriguing. Here copper workings long antedate the coming of the white man. Along the southern shore Keweenaw Peninsula prongs upward for fifty miles like the fang of a rattlesnake. The red men knew its rich copper deposits and sometimes excavated trenches thirty feet deep. This malleable metal foreshadowed their emancipation from the Stone Age. Across the lake, almost within the shadow of Thunder Cape, millions of dollars' worth of silver have been mined. But that prosaic metal, iron, has yielded more fabulous riches. Southward lie the Menominee and Gogebic iron ranges, while westward are the peerless Mesabi deposits, which have given America its commanding lead in the Age of Steel.

Superior is the gateway to the Canadian Northwest. At Fort William and Port Arthur on Thunder Bay grain elevators with a capacity of millions of bushels collect rich harvests from Saskatchewan and Manitoba. From the forested shores great rafts comprising a million logs drift like floating islands to markets farther south. Fisheries have been noteworthy since the days when the Ojibways set their rude nets or dropped their hooks through holes in the ice. Among various species salmon trout are the most important.

Prior to the year 1855 there was little commerce on Superior. Between the big lake and Huron the fall of twenty feet presented impassable rapids. Now several huge locks ranging side by side in the famous Soo Canal (Sault Ste. Marie) absorb eighteen feet of that descent in the space of half a mile. These locks maintain the lake level, while through them passes an endless procession of ore steamers from Duluth and grain carriers from Port William. Such basic commodities are supplemented by many others, while the steamers return laden with coal and innumerable manufactured goods. This canal, though closed for several months each year, now boasts a greater tonnage than the Suez and Panama canals combined. The rude portage where Brulé and Radisson dragged their canoes has become one of the busiest highways in the world.

MICHIGAN

Lake Michigan is long—307 miles—with a maximum width of 118. From the northwest Green Bay opens into the hinterland as though it intended to become a separate lake, then changed its mind. On the opposite shore Grand Traverse Bay began a similar penetration into the state of Michigan, but abandoned the attempt. Otherwise, the 1300-mile shore line is free from important indentations.

Opposite the entrance to Green Bay and about midway across the lake the sounding line has run out just short of 154 fathoms, or 923 feet. This is the deepest pocket so far discovered. The average depth, however, 276 feet, gives the lake a volume of 1165 cubic miles. Though in area, 22,400 square miles, it yields to Huron, its water content is considerably greater. Its drainage basin, 69,040 square miles, is slightly smaller than that of Huron, the annual rainfall identical, 30 inches. In fact, though quite unlike in outline, Michigan and Huron are almost twin lakes.

This is apparent in their elevation above sea level, which is just short of 580 feet. Oddly enough, although Michigan drains into Huron through the historic Straits of Mackinac, its average level is nearly half an inch lower. Mackinac Island, which guards the strait, was a favorite meeting place of Indian tribes and a position of great importance in opening up the northwest. The most powerful lighthouse in inland waters— 3,000,000 candle power—stands on this island.

The southeastern shore of Lake Michigan is fringed with curious lagoons which penetrate several miles into the mainland. Some are vestiges of the greater lake which once overflowed the present shore line. Others are the enlarged mouths of little rivers, for the state of Michigan pours over two thousand streams into the four Great Lakes which touch its scattered borders. Still farther south is a picturesque region of sand dunes which suggest some wind-tormented seacoast.

On the Jesuit map of 1672 Michigan appears as Lac Ilinois, for a local Indian tribe. Its present name, however, was soon preferred.

The lake was the scene of many romantic exploits in the days of La Salle. He was the first to recognize the importance of the Great Lakes as trade routes, and hoped to link them with the Mississippi in a vast French empire. Sailing down the Father of Waters, he established the colony of Louisiana, named for the king of France, and, like most daring spirits of the time, died with his boots on, murdered by mutinous followers.

In memory of such exploits Chicago turns a longing eye toward the Mississippi, to dream of a deeper than the present drainage canal with the prospect of yet greater commerce.

How this metropolis arose from the swamps of old Fort Dearborn is an amazing phenomenon. But Lake Michigan boasts other notable cities: Milwaukee in Wisconsin; Gary, Indiana, with its smoke-belching steel mills; Escanaba, whose ore steamers, loading Michigan's rich iron deposits, compete for that metallic harvest with Duluth; and others. But indeed, with minerals and forest products, cattle and grain, and the innumerable manufacturing interests of a complex civilization, Lake Michigan is the heart of one of the busiest regions on earth.

The other Great Lakes are on the Canadian border. Michigan alone lies wholly within the United States. Could Jean Nicolet, who first crossed its waters more than three centuries ago, see them today, his disappointment would be swallowed up in growing wonder. True, he failed to discover the Northwest Passage or to present the compliments of Louis at the ancient court of China. But he did open a route to another empire of incalculable resources.

HURON

Huron seems undecided whether to be one lake or two. A narrow peninsula stretching northwest for sixty miles and a chain of islands reaching eastward from the Soo Strait nearly divide it. The smaller portion, Georgian Bay, named for George IV of England, extends westward through the North Channel; the main body of the lake is more regular in outline, although Saginaw Bay projects like a sore thumb into the state of Michigan. The name Huron commemorates the unfortunate

Indian tribe whose almost total extermination by the Iroquois
was one of the bloodiest chapters in Indian warfare.

Huron is the broadest of the Great Lakes, excelling even
Superior. Though its length is but 206 miles, its extreme width
is 183. Besides, it has the longest shore line of any of the Great
Lakes—2300 miles.

Huron ranks second to Superior, its area, 23,010 square
miles, slightly shading that of Michigan. Second also is its
drainage basin, 72,420 square miles, with an annual rainfall of
30 inches. Its greatest depth is 750 feet; the average, 195, gives
it a volume of about 851 cubic miles.

No other lake in the world encloses an island so large as
Huron's Grand Manitoulin. Eighty miles long, with an area of
1223 square miles, it almost equals the state of Rhode Island.
In fact it includes over a hundred lakes of its own, one, Mani-
tou, being quite ten miles long. The island presents a bluff
tableland, terminating in steep cliffs. Formerly it was a headquarters of the Ottawa Indians, perhaps the most active traders
of their race. Forests of pine, cedar, and various hardwoods
supply an important lumber industry, while more than half a
million dollars are invested in fisheries. Georgian Bay is noted
for its whitefish.

The shores of this bay are particularly beautiful in the south,
where thousands of islands open up innumerable wooded
vistas. Toward the north the Canadian Shield intrudes its
rugged hills and barrens.

Bruce Peninsula, which partially divides Georgian Bay from
larger Huron, is of eroded limestone, terminating in the bold
bluff known as Lion Head. At the extreme tip are two natural
harbors called Big Tub and Little Tub.

Huron was the first of the Great Lakes to be explored by
the white man, for the Ottawa River, with its comparatively
short portage to Lake Nipissing, was a natural highway for
birch-bark canoes all the way from Montreal. Yet it is the

least developed of the Great Lakes. No city of major size has sprung up along its shores, where long stretches remain as wild as at the coming of Brulé and Champlain.

Receiving the waters of Superior and Michigan in addition to its own, Huron pours 174,000 cubic feet a second into the St. Claire River. This presently expands as Lake St. Claire, a roughly circular body of water 26 miles across, with an area of 460 square miles. As its average depth, however, is only 10 feet, a channel 21 feet deep is maintained for navigation.

Lake St. Claire empties·in turn into the Detroit River, the site of one of the major manufacturing centers of the world. And this river, teeming with traffic, continues southward to empty into Lake Erie.

ERIE

Unlike the other Great Lakes, which are deep as well as extensive, Erie is a gigantic puddle. About seven miles off the sandy tip of Long Point, it attains its maximum depth, 210 feet, but the average is only 58. Hence the water content is but 109 cubic miles or little more than one thirtieth Superior's volume.

While Superior, Michigan, and Huron are of the select group of lacustrine giants, Erie and Ontario belong to the secondary category. Still, Erie ranks as number twelve in the list of the world's big lakes, with an area just under 10,000 square miles, or 9940 to be exact. To revert to dry statistics, its extreme length is 248 miles, its width 57, its coast line 800. Its drainage basin, 34,680 square miles, has an annual rainfall of 33 inches.

A curious topographical feature is Long Point, really an island, which projects a ridge of sand dunes from the Canadian shore for twenty miles into the lake. It forms a glacial moraine sculptured by winds and waves like the barrier beaches of Martha's Vineyard or Long Island in New York.

Erie's average elevation above the sea is just under 572 feet. Since 1900 there has been a variation of nearly five feet between its extreme high and low. Erie is some eight feet lower than Huron, a difference accounted for by the southward current of the connecting St. Claire and Detroit rivers.

Since waterfalls are a frequent accompaniment of lake structure, it is fitting that the Great Lakes should possess one of the grandest waterfalls on earth. Just how Niagara compares with Victoria Falls in South Africa or Iguassú in South America is a theme of argument with world travelers. Whatever spectacular features other falls may present, Niagara is more accessible, while its magnificent play of waters is an open panorama. Artificial floodlights enhance its beauty at night, and winter, which groins and chisels its frozen surface into innumerable prisms of ice, adds a unique touch of splendor.

Niagara is linked with Lake Erie in a destructive partnership, for the falls unceasingly plot the latter's destruction. Now and again great chunks of tough limestone, which forms the flooring of the river, crash into the seething gulf below. At the present rate of erosion, four or five feet annually, the river, within ten thousand years, would gnaw a channel all the way back to Erie, sufficient to drain off its shallow content and change it to a silted river valley. Geologists assure us, however, that the limestone strata dips toward the west, so that the great falls will subside to a mere rapids long before the lake itself is involved in ruin.

Since Erie is much the shallowest, it is the most treacherous of the Great Lakes. Its waters react to sudden squalls. Protracted storms in the winter of 1899–1900 heaped them along exposed shores to a height of seven feet two inches above normal levels.

This condition is the more regrettable because Erie saw the first development of lake commerce upon an important scale, and is still a focus of busy navigation. How La Salle launched his tiny ship, the *Griffon*, upon its waters has already been recounted. But the forerunner of the vast fleets of steam vessels which now ply the waters of the Great Lakes was that creation of Robert Fulton built in 1818 and named for a Wyandotte chieftain "Walk on the Water." True, she would seem archaic now compared with modern leviathans, for the Great Lakes have evolved a type all their own: whaleback oil tankers and ore carriers which remain seaworthy even with their decks awash.

Numerous cities have sprung up along the shore. There is Erie in Pennsylvania; Ohio has Sandusky, a connection by river with Toledo, and the great port of Cleveland, whose population hovers about the million mark. Buffalo in New York is the Eastern portal of much Great Lakes commerce. The Erie Canal was once the most important highway to the West.

Lake Erie was the site of a naval engagement in the War of 1812, when six small British warships, under Commander Barclay, were defeated by nine American vessels, rather poorly equipped, under Admiral Perry. The latter's classic comment, "We have met the enemy and they are ours," has thrilled many a schoolboy in his study of American history.

Fortunately Erie's shores no longer echo to cannon fire. A saner period dawned when the treaty between Great Britain and the United States stipulated that the Canadian border should remain unfortified and that the waters of the border lakes should be open to both nations. That international boundary is a symbol of enduring peace.

ONTARIO

Ontario, last, and in area the smallest of the five Great Lakes, presents some novel features. While Superior is over 602 feet above the sea and even Erie nearly 572, Ontario's elevation is less than 246. The swift Niagara River, with its rapids and above all the tremendous waterfall, accounts for this abrupt descent.

Ontario is 196 miles long by 53 wide. Like Erie and Superior, its long axis is roughly from east to west (those of Huron and Michigan are rather north and south). Its waters are clear, cool, and intensely blue.

Although Ontario's area is only 7540 square miles, it is relatively deep. Some twenty-two miles west of and a little north of the city of Oswego the sounding line plummets downward 778 feet. Its average depth is 264 against Erie's 58, so that it contains more than three times as much water as its larger but shallower companion, or roughly 377 cubic miles. Its shore line is also greater than Erie's—1100 miles. Ontario's drainage basin is 34,640 square miles; the annual rainfall 34 inches.

The northern coast is rather bold. Twelve miles east of Toronto, Scarborough Bluffs loom two hundred feet above the water. They are not rock, however, but glacial clay in which countless bank swallows have excavated their nests.

Along the New York shores dwelt the formidable Iroquois, who regarded Ontario as a private domain and warred incessantly against neighboring tribes. Farther south glacial relics include the so-called Finger Lakes, long, narrow, and almost Alpine in their beauty. Two of these, Seneca and Cayuga, commemorate members of the original Five Nations. Two other tribes, the Oneidas and Onondagas, have lakes farther to the east, while the fierce Mohawks are remembered in the river of that name which swells the current of the Hudson.

Champlain called Ontario Lac Louis, but the name failed to stick. Fort Frontenac upon its western shores was a strategic point in the romantic days of Anglo-French rivalry and lurid Indian warfare. It was the site of the earliest shipping enterprise on the Great Lakes. More important towns now grace the coasts. Oswego is a busy port on the New York side, while Rochester, connected by river, is only a few miles distant. The true mistress of the lake, however, is Toronto, the second city of Canada.

Niagara and its series of cataracts, once an impossible barrier, was long since by-passed by the Welland Canal, with huge locks. These have made possible a continuous passage for ships of 14-foot draught from the headwaters of Superior to the sea.

Toward the northeast the waters of Ontario, swelled by the influx of the other Great Lakes, pour through the forested corridors of the Thousand Islands. There the St. Lawrence begins its majestic progress to the sea. Nor is the story complete without mention of the port of Montreal, metropolis of all Canada and of quaint, unspoiled Quebec, secure upon its lofty heights. For these cities are the eastern sentinels of the Northwest, or rather the gateway of approach from the Old World to the New through its matchless watercourse of inland seas.

NIPIGON, A SPORTSMAN'S PARADISE

If Nipigon were somewhere else, it would be an outstanding feature of the landscape. Sequestered among Canada's countless other lakes, and eclipsed by gigantic Superior, it is not so well known as it should be.

Few big lakes are more beautiful. Roughly oval—about 60 miles long by 45 wide—its shore line is extremely irregular. On the north Ombabika Bay, nearly twenty miles long, joins the parent lake through an opening scarcely a mile wide. Deep bays also indent the southwestern shore, including Kaiashki, almost landlocked, Chief Bay, and McIntyre Bay. Over a thousand islands dot the surface. Kelvin is about ten miles long, while other large islands are Geike, Murchison, and Logan.

Toward the north the shores blend into lengthening slopes and rolling hills; toward the south and west they are marked by bluff headlands and forested with spruce, fir, tamarack, and white birch. Many streams bring the overflow of lesser lakes from the remoter hinterland.

Nipigon's elevation is 813 feet above Superior, only thirty-five miles distant, into which it drains through the Nipigon River, tumbling down a series of cascades. These foaming waters and sheltered pools are a favorite haunt of fish and much frequented by anglers.

The river empties into Nipigon Bay, one of those rugged indentations along Superior's northern coast. A chain of islands, including St. Ignace and Simpson, make this bay almost a separate lake, whose boundaries are cliffs hundreds of feet high.

In glacial times Nipigon was a northern spur of Superior, or rather of that super lake Algonquin. The Nipigon River remains Superior's principal feeder and Lake Nipigon an integral part of the Great Lakes system.

Strictly on its own account it deserves a place among the world's big lakes, for its area as given by the Canadian Cyclopedia is 1590 square miles, while other authorities suggest a somewhat larger figure.

In the Indian tongue Nipigon means "deep, clear water." Wonderfully blue and transparent, it is deep, for toward the southern and western shores the sounding line has run out 540 feet without touching bottom.

The first white settlement was a rude stockade called La Tourette, built near the outlet in 1678 by Claude Greysolon, brother of the founder of Duluth. This fort was designed to check the Hudson's Bay Company from the north, for those pioneering days brought bloody clashes between the British monopoly and determined independents. A larger trading post was later established on a point of land projecting from the northwestern shore.

Furs are no longer the major industry of a region which presents rich lumbering, stock raising, and agricultural resources, while as a recreational center Nipigon offers unsurpassed advantages.

THE MIGHTY MACKENZIE

Three of the world's big lakes drain into the Mackenzie River. Beginning with Athabaska, less than half as large as Ontario, they increase in size as one goes north, for Great Slave is larger than Erie, while Great Bear, with its desolate upper bays extending beyond the Arctic Circle, is probably still more extensive.

The river basin occupies much of the mid-continental plain which separates the Canadian Shield toward the east from the Rockies to the west. This region, roughly triangular, is hundreds of miles wide at the south, but on the shores of the Arctic, where the Shield approaches the mountainous highlands of Alaska, it narrows to little more than a hundred.

The Mackenzie River is 2525 miles long, while its basin measures 682,000 square miles. From the south one branch, the Athabaska, winds for 740 miles to Athabaska Lake. From the west another branch, the Peace River, more than a thousand miles long, breaks through the gorges of the Rockies to join the Great Slave River on its way to Great Slave Lake. Issuing from that lake, the main stream of the Mackenzie flows northward like those huge Siberian rivers, the Ob, the Lena, and the Yenisei. From the west it receives the Liard, 650 miles long, the Pelly, and other considerable affluents, from the east the Great Bear River, with the overflow of that huge lake, until, through several mouths which may be choked with ice even in midsummer, it pours 500,000 cubic feet of water a second into the frozen Arctic.

The river is named for Alexander Mackenzie, a young Scotchman who came to the New World as a clerk in the employ of the Montreal Fur Company, a competitor of the Hudson's Bay Company. On June 3, 1789, he set out from Fort Chippewyan on Lake Athabaska, hoping to find the Northwest Passage to the Pacific. His canoes were capacious craft, so large that one of them bore four tons of trade goods. In one canoe were a German and four Canadians with two of their wives; in another an Indian chief, his two wives, and two young Indians; other Indians manned a third canoe. Mackenzie himself paced off the portage around the dangerous rapids in Great Slave River. In Great Slave Lake he groped for days through fog and ice, seeking the outlet, while his companions bailed desperately with an old iron kettle. Entering the river which bears his name, he noted the beetling ramparts where the current seethes for five miles between limestone cliffs 150 feet high. At one place his moccasins were mired by petroleum oozing from the soil, evidence of that "liquid gold" which has intrigued prospectors ever since. He passed the point where Great Bear River swings around Bear Rock, a towering sentinel 1400 feet high, to mingle with the larger stream, and some miles farther on noticed a coal seam afire in the river bank, ignited perhaps by lightning or campfires: a wasteful conflagration that has been smoldering ever since. He had trouble with native paddlers who tried to dissuade him from his mad enterprise by direful tales of "winged men who killed by the eye," and bloody feuds with nomadic Eskimos. Some of the natives he encountered impressed him favorably. The Gravel River Indians built enormous canoes, 30 feet long and 6 or 7 broad, of moose hides stretched over spruce frames and lashed with moose-hide thongs. Fish abounded in both river and lakes.

At length, through one of the many channels that opened windowlike from the broad delta, he gazed out into the Arctic, where he observed whales, probably white whales or belugas, spouting among the ice floes. But no thrill of achievement was his. On the contrary, he named the great stream the River of Disappointment, for he had hoped it might make a wide sweep to the Pacific. Instead, he noted in his journal, "It was evident that these waters emptied themselves into the Hyperborean Sea."

Returning to Fort Chippewyan after an absence of only 102 days, during which he had traveled more than three thousand miles, the young explorer (he was only twenty-six) still turned eager glances westward. Four years later, in 1793, he started on another journey of discovery down the valleys of the Peace and Fraser rivers to the Pacific. On a rock on the seacoast he inscribed in letters still legible, "Alexander Mackenzie from Canada by land the twenty-second July one thousand seven hundred and ninety-three." This memorable excursion antedated by several years the better-advertised exploit of Lewis and Clark, and gave him the distinction of being the first white man to cross the continent north of Mexico.

Shrewder or more fortunate than many who perished in unfamiliar waters or left their bones in the wilderness, Mackenzie returned to Scotland, where he was knighted and passed his declining years in peace.

ATHABASKA

Across the northern borders of the Canadian provinces of
Alberta and Saskatchewan stretches the most southerly of the
three Great Lakes that feed the Mackenzie River. It is named
Athabaska for the Indian tribe that once roamed its lonely
shores or hooked whitefish through the ice.

Though its maximum width is 32 miles, its major axis
extends east and west for 195. Formerly it was even longer, for
the Claire and other lakes have been cut off by the silted deltas
of the Peace and Athabaska rivers to remind us how readily
streams may fill up and obliterate even large lakes.

The Britannica gives Athabaska an area of 3085 miles, a
figure slightly reduced in other estimates. Scattered soundings
indicate an extreme depth of 300 feet, while the altitude above
sea level is 695.

The southern shore of the lake rises abruptly to the surrounding plain some 500 feet above. The northern shore is of
more recent origin, with many indentations and islands. Toward the east the Canadian Shield appears in steep cliffs 400
feet high.

Athabaska was originally a meeting place of rivers. From
the east comes the Stone or Black River bearing surplus waters
from Lake Wollaston. Other streams are the Old Fort, the
Gaudet, and the Grand Rapids. Here the waters are clear and
blue, but toward the western extremity, where the Athabaska
River pours in its silted torrents, they are muddy and in places
very shallow.

The outlet, near the western end, is the so-called Rocky
River, 150 yards wide, which soon unites with the Peace to
become the Great Slave River flowing northward into Great
Slave Lake. Midway in its course occurs the only break in

navigation clear to the Arctic, where a series of cascades inter-rupted by a sixteen-foot drop includes the Rapids of the Drowned. This evil name was bestowed in 1786 when two canoes on their way to Fort Resolution on Great Slave Lake capsized and five men perished in the boiling waters.

In the spring of 1778 that indomitable trader and explorer, Peter Pond, set off with four canoes laden with trade goods to find Lake Athabaska. The expedition was financed by Saskatchewan traders. According to Mackenzie, Pond built his post on the river about thirty miles from the lake. In 1787 he also seems to have visited Great Slave Lake, heard of its outlet, and wondered if this might not be the river, mentioned by Captain Cook, which flowed into the Pacific. Thus he blazed the trail for Mackenzie's later explorations. Pond, a hardy pioneer, ruthless perhaps from necessity, was suspected of murdering two white men. Whatever the facts or the occasion, he failed to make his fortune and died in poverty at Milford, Connecticut, in 1807.

Alexander Mackenzie, who succeeded Pond in 1788, built Fort Chippewyan on the southern shores of the lake, which was pretty thoroughly explored by Philip Turner from 1790 to 1792.

Mackenzie called Athabaska the Lake of the Hills, a name descriptive of much surrounding terrain. Incidentally, it was from Chippewyan that he set out on his epoch-making voyages to the Arctic and Pacific oceans. Modern Chippewyan, with its whitewashed walls, has been moved to the northern shore, not far from the lake outlet.

Athabaska was noted for its fish before the coming of the white man. The annual catch, according to a recent Canadian bulletin, exceeds 2,500,000 pounds; it is mainly trout and whitefish.

In former years scores of flat-bottomed scows came blun-dering up the Athabaska River loaded with freight and supplies. Fifty feet long by 12 wide, they were equipped with four 22-foot oars. The current, however, was the main motive power, while the principal function of the 35-foot steering sweep was to avoid innumerable shoals and sand bars. Arrived at the lake, these bulky craft were broken up for building lumber.

The lake begins to freeze in October and is not wholly free from ice until June.

Steamers of shallow draught now ply its surface as well as long stretches of the Peace and Athabaska rivers. Similar craft beyond the rapids navigate the Mackenzie nearly to its mouth. Airplanes speed far more rapidly over vast vacant spaces, while more modern stations are superseding Hudson's Bay stockades. But commercial activity still lags behind the potential resources of this great river with its imposing lakes.

GREAT SLAVE LAKE

On Christmas Eve in the year 1771 Samuel Hearne, a young man in the employ of the Hudson's Bay Company, emerged from the wilderness to gaze across a vast lake whose further shores lay hidden beyond the horizon. Called by the Indians Athapusco, which means "Grass and Reeds Here and There," it is better known as Great Slave Lake.

Oddly enough, Hearne approached it from the frozen north. More than a year before he had left Fort Prince of Wales at the mouth of the Churchill, to seek a "far-away metal river" (the Coppermine) which emptied into a "vast sea" (the Arctic) where "the tide ebbed and flowed."

His journey was an epic of fortitude and endurance. A band of Indians accompanied him, led by Matonabbee, a giant savage with all the virtues and vices of his race. Squaws were taken along "to drag the sleds," for Matonabbee had no illusions about women's rights. "Women were made for labor," he affirmed, adding, "One of them can carry or haul as much as two men can do." Hence he was usually accompanied by from five to eight wives, all of them, according to Hearne, "strapping Amazons."

Crossing the great barren ground, the party killed an occasional caribou or musk ox. At times they subsisted upon "moss water," a dismal soup made from the scant vegetation of the tundra; at times they simply starved.

Other Indians joined them. At Bloody Falls on the Coppermine they massacred an encampment of Eskimos, an outrage which Hearne was powerless to prevent. One young girl, transfixed by lances, clasped his legs, "writhing like a spitted eel," but all that the horror-stricken Englishman could do for her was to persuade an Indian to put a merciful end to her sufferings.

Hearne, who was the first man to approach the Arctic from the land side, wrote, "At the mouth of the river the sea is full of islands and shoals as far as I could see with the assistance of a good pocket telescope."

Returning over a different route, the party hastened by forced marches across the desolate barrens. One ailing woman twice crawled into camp late at night, but the third time failed to appear. Footsore and exhausted, Hearne was compelled to keep the pace or be left behind in that merciless wilderness. His moccasins frayed the skin from his feet, while the raw soles became honeycombed with twigs and gravel. His toenails festered and several fell off. Such was the lot of the explorer in the old, romantic days of the Hudson's Bay Company.

Hearne lingered for two weeks on the shores of the vast lake he had discovered. He thought it might be 300 miles long by 60 wide, a conservative estimate, as it is really 325 by 70. He was also impressed by the glory of the Northern Lights with their distinct crackling sound like "the waving of a large flag in a gale of wind."

Hearne found the lake filled with islands, "most of which are clothed with fine tall poplars, birch, and pine, and are well stocked with Indian deer." He noted the "great quantity of very fine fish," including the largest trout he had ever seen, while of the pike he wrote, "If I say that some of these fish were upward of forty pounds weight I am sure I do not exceed the truth." The party crossed from one red granite island to another, reaching the southern shore on January 9. South of the lake they encountered wood buffalo and moose that "were harder to kill." Returning to Fort Prince of Wales after an absence of eighteen months and twenty-three days, the young explorer was rewarded by the company with two hundred pounds sterling and immediately dispatched on a fresh expedition.

In 1785 Peter Pond sent Laurent Leroux and Cuthbert Grant to erect a rude structure on the southern shore of Great Slave Lake. Alexander Mackenzie, however, seems to have been the first to explore the western sector on his voyage to the Arctic in 1789. He observed that the Cree Indians, adopting the warlike prowess of the Iroquois, had spread their conquests over a great area of western Canada. Slave was their term of reproach for the Athabaskan aborigines. As there was a lesser Slave Lake much farther south, this body of water became Great Slave Lake.

Admiral Sir George Back, who explored the Back River which empties into the Arctic, spent the winter of 1833–34 at Fort Reliance on the eastern extremity of the lake. He wrote, "Its length is nearly equal to that of Lake Michigan [it is really somewhat longer] and it may therefore be considered one of the secondary lakes of North America." The good admiral might have included the rest of the world in that comparison.

Perhaps no other big lake has varied so widely in its estimated area. This has ranged all the way from 7100 to 13,400 square miles. A recent edition of the Britannica gives it as 9770 (slightly smaller than Lake Erie). The American Cyclopedia, however, prefers 10,100, while the Canadian Cyclopedia, which has the advantage of being nearest the subject of discussion, says 11,170. This latter figure is confirmed by the Hydrographic Service of the Canadian government. So far it has been impossible to make any exact triangulation of its shores, which in some places are not only marshy and ill defined but fluctuate with changing water levels. The eastern portion is traversed by narrow, rocky peninsulas interspersed with deep channels culminating in McLeods Bay, which suggest definite faulting of the earth crust.

The lake lies at an elevation of 391 feet. Few soundings are available. The broad western sector (the main axis runs roughly east and west) is relatively shallow; the greatest depths are to be found in the eastern end, where the waters are beautifully clear. Here they invade the Canadian Shield, with Sentinel Point rising over a thousand feet. And here in Christie Bay the sounding line plunges downward for 2015 feet, much deeper than Superior. Innumerable rocky islands include the favored group known as the Blessed Isles, because they are free from the prevalent swarms of black flies. The shores are sparsely wooded, although dense thickets cluster in sheltered ravines. Toward the northeast stretch the bleak barrens whence the Hoarfrost River comes tumbling over a 60-foot precipice.

The southern side receives several rivers including the Snowdrift, the Big and Little Buffalo, and the Hay. The latter river, at a point some twenty miles below the lake, catapults over two falls, the first 46, the second 105 feet high, to foam through a narrow gorge that suggests Niagara. The principal feeder, however, is the Great Slave River, which brings the waters of Lake Athabaska and the remote reaches of the Peace River, fed by the snows of the Canadian Rockies. Here the marshy shores are often clotted with windrows of driftwood.

On the north a great spur projects more than a hundred miles into a mountainous terrain to receive the waters of the Yellow Knife and other streams. A similar spur once extended southward to give the lake some resemblance to a gigantic cross. This arm, however, has been silted up by the Great Slave River, which also encroaches through its several mouths upon the main body of the lake.

Although the basin is glacial, some of it is of more ancient origin, eroded by rivers now unknown. A. E. Cameron has traced in beaches on the surrounding country the outlines of a vaster lake which included not only Great Slave but Athabaska also. Then both the Mackenzie and the Nelson River outlets were dammed by the Keewatin icecap, so that water levels rose eight hundred feet or more.

Fish have always abounded in Great Slave Lake, and as early as 1887 McConnell estimated the annual catch at half a million pounds. Gold-bearing quartz, with deposits of zinc and lead, suggest still undiscovered mineral wealth.

The climate is not unusually severe. While the mercury in winter sometimes sinks to 40 below, it is much colder farther south. Snow, which falls in October, seldom accumulates to a depth of more than two or three feet. The lake also freezes at that time, the western area thawing in June, the eastern somewhat later. Summer temperatures may soar to 90 and the lowlands become gay with flowers.

There are few settlements. Fort Resolution stands near the mouth of the Great Slave River, Fort Ray on the northern spur. The white population, mainly traders, missionaries, and government employees, probably does not exceed five hundred. The surrounding country is almost as unbroken as in the days of Samuel Hearne. At that time it was a notable game center, but wild life is now so reduced that a trapper trekking fifty miles on snowshoes recently reported no trace of any living thing, not even a vagrant rabbit.

The same fate would have befallen that most representative of North American animals, the bison, had not the Canadian government in 1922 set apart a great game sanctuary of 17,300 square miles approaching within twenty-five miles of the southern shore of Great Slave Lake. Here the wood bison, somewhat darker and slightly larger than the plains variety, have so multiplied that a census in 1934 reported 8000 individuals. Old bulls had attained a weight of 2500 pounds.

Some overflow from Great Slave Lake finds its way to Hudson Bay through the Ark-i-linik River, but the major outlet is the Mackenzie. Here that vast stream is eight or ten miles wide, compassing marshy islands where the muskeg moss has accumulated to a reported depth of ten feet. River steamers now ply its waters, while the airplane is beginning to spy out the surrounding wilderness. For metal wings can span in a few hours what Samuel Hearne on swollen feet could traverse only through many toilsome months.

GREAT BEAR LAKE

The largest and loneliest of Canadian lakes lies hidden in the far northern solitudes on the rim of the barren ground. It is called Great Bear Lake. The name suggests some specimen of that surly animal slain by Indian or early voyageur, for black bears still lurk in spruce thickets to the south, while a variety known as *Ursus Richardsoni* roams the treeless wastes toward the northeast. This vast lake, however, owes its name to none of these, but to the greatest of all bears, Ursa Major, that frosty constellation which dominates the northern sky;

an appropriate choice, for the lake extends some distance beyond the Arctic Circle.

The shore line, formed by five bays which radiate from a common center, is extremely irregular. Four of these bays, beginning in the northwest and proceeding clockwise, are known respectively as Smith, Dease, MacTavish, and Keith. They would give the lake the appearance of a squat hourglass were it not that a fifth indentation, McVicar, pronging far to the south, rather suggests a five-armed amoeba. The Canadian Cyclopedia, drawing data from government reports, gives the lake an area of 11,660 square miles; more recent estimates top 13,000, for surveys in the wilderness are still sketchy and ill defined. But the Canadian Hydrographic and Map Service sets the figure at 11,490. In any case, Great Bear Lake is entitled to membership among the world's major bodies of fresh water, ranking just behind Baikal and Tanganyika.

Its length is usually given as 195 miles, its depth as 270 feet. The latter figure is based upon soundings made by Dr. Richardson more than a century ago, although in MacTavish Bay his 45-fathom line failed to reach bottom. A. E. Porsild, however, who spent some months on Dease Bay in 1932, found the average of 65 soundings ranging from 300 to 360 feet. As the elevation of the lake surface is about 200, the bottom is depressed below the level of the Arctic Ocean.

The lake is the focus of a considerable watershed 400 miles in diameter. Its most useful tributaries seem to be the Camsell River, flowing into MacTavish Bay from the south to open up a portage to Great Slave Lake, and the Dease, a shallow stream entering Dease Bay which affords laborious passage by canoe to the Coppermine River and the ocean. From Keith Bay, in the southwest, the lake empties into the Great Bear River by a channel 200 yards wide, excavated through banks of sand and clay. An ice dam thirty feet thick forms across the river in winter and ice cliffs fringe its rapid current even in midsummer. E. C. Cabot also found some outflow through the ancient Hare River basin farther north, connecting Smith Bay with the Mackenzie. This example of "dual drainage" occurs elsewhere in this area of glacial disturbance.

In 1799 Mackenzie is believed to have established a trading post on the shores of Great Bear Lake. Near this site stood Fort Franklin, named for Sir John Franklin, who wintered there in 1825–26 as a base of operations for exploring the bleak seacoast, the threshold of that region where he was to perish with all his party some years later in the most appalling of Arctic tragedies. His companion, Dr. Richardson, made many observations, noting that songbirds returning in the spring serenaded their mates only at midnight, while they were silent the remaining twenty-four hours.

Doctor Richardson again wintered in this region in 1848–49 at a post built for him by Warren Dease, chief factor of the Hudson's Bay Company, on the extreme northeast corner of the lake.

J. Mackintosh Bell explored the northern and eastern shores in 1901. Starting on June 23 at Smith Bay, north of that bulging peninsula known as the Scented Grass Hills, he was delayed by ice until July 4. Ice again delayed him along the northern shore until July 23. There he discovered a cache of caribou meat left by Eskimos and noted the blossoming of innumerable flowers. Much of this otherwise dreary region was treeless, but the southern shores of Dease Bay were sparsely wooded. In the main, however, gravel hills with boulders and other relics of the Ice Age marked a landscape that justified the description of Father Petitot, priest to the aborigines, who called it "the most desolate region I ever journeyed in," while he referred to the vast expanse of fresh waters as "that Arctic Caspian."

In contrast with Great Slave Lake, Great Bear has few islands, while its basin is generally deeper, its coasts more

clearly defined. Though sprawling over the valley of the Mackenzie, it indents the massive Canadian Shield where Mac-
Tavish Bay reveals that continental escarpment in cliffs a
thousand feet high.

In 1901 Dr. Bell wrote, "In the greenstone east of Mac-
Tavish Bay . . . the steep rocky shores . . . are often
stained with cobalt blue and copper green." That chance sug-
gestion of hidden treasure led Gilbert La Bine to visit the
region by airplane in 1930. Three years later Hope Plant was
established, to be superseded by Eldorado Plant on what is
now La Bine Point, where are the richest deposits of pitch-
blende known anywhere on earth.

At this mine, on the south shores of Cameron Bay, somewhat
sheltered by spruce forests, a little settlement of miners and
their associates brave the Arctic winter. The ore, though rich
in silver, is chiefly prized as the source of that costliest of
metals, radium. Six and a half tons produce one gram of this
luminous mineral, a meager harvest seemingly, until we compare it with yields of one gram to forty tons in the Belgian
Congo or one hundred and twenty-eight tons in the richest
deposits so far discovered in the United States.

Supplies for this remote settlement have been laboriously
ferried down the Mackenzie River, up the turbulent Great
Bear, and so across the lake, taking advantage of that uncertain period when its waters were freed from ice. But the
airplane has developed more dependable communication with
the outer world, so that costly mineral concentrates are now
winged southward to provide necessary supplies on the return
journey.

Chill winds sweep Great Bear Lake. Masses of driftwood
accumulate along its southern shores. The waters respond to
tremors like the familiar seiches of Alpine lakes. Porsild found
at the mouth of Dease Bay a rhythmical rise and fall of eight
inches, noting eight such spasmodic "tides" in the space of

five days. Narrow channels fretted by resultant currents apparently never freeze.

All authorities comment upon the crystal clearness of the waters, so transparent that a whitish object submerged ninety feet is readily visible. At the outlet these waters are a greenish blue. Everywhere they swarm with fish, including herring, while whitefish, salmon, and other varieties await the sportsman who rarely comes.

The vast countryside is sparsely peopled. Besides the mining settlement, Fort Norman, a Hudson's Bay trading post, stands across the lake on Keith Bay, near the outlet. The poverty-stricken Hare Indians roam the valley of the Mackenzie to the west, while toward the south migrant members of the Dog Rib tribe are occasionally encountered. Eskimos sometimes visit Dease Bay, but northward to the Arctic, scarcely a hundred and fifty miles distant, stretches a tenantless region of sparse soil and sparser vegetation; of glacier-smoothed and -rounded hills; of nameless and almost numberless lakes.

THE NELSON-SASKATCHEWAN SYSTEM

One of the major fresh-water systems of the world drains into Hudson Bay through the broad estuary of the Nelson River. Far to the west the many-branched Saskatchewan collects the melted snows of the Rockies to hurry them onward to Lake Winnipeg, which is considerably larger than Ontario. These waters emerge as the Nelson to traverse the Canadian Shield and levy tribute from many other lakes. Foaming down its last cascade ninety miles from the sea, the swollen current broadens to three or four miles, increasing to six or seven at the mouth, where it buffets fifteen-foot tides from Hudson Bay.

The barren seacoast was explored by the English admiral Sir Thomas Button in 1612–13. When his mate, Nelson, died, the admiral had him buried on the shore, a lonely grave now remembered in a mighty river.

The region is rich in lore of the Hudson's Bay Company. Pierre Radisson, who voyaged into Lake Superior to tap the wealth of the great Northwest, returned a millionaire with "six hundred thousand beaver skins" only to be despoiled by the French governor. Smarting at what he considered highhanded injustices, Radisson vainly sought redress at the court of Louis, then fled to London. There his rude eloquence so enthused Charles II that an expedition was dispatched from Gravesend on June 3, 1668. Two years later the "Merry Monarch" issued a charter to "the governor and company of gentlemen adventurers trading into Hudson's Bay." And so the dream of a penniless expatriate took form in a vast empire of the New World.

A rude stockade called Fort Charles was erected on James Bay, to be followed by more pretentious Rupert House. But the shallow waters were hazardous to shipping, while farther north great rivers like the Nelson and the Churchill opened more inviting trade routes into the interior. Hence York Factory was established at the mouth of the Nelson and Fort Prince of Wales on the Churchill, while young Samuel Hearne, recently returned from his discovery of Great Slave Lake, was dispatched into the remote hinterland to build Cumberland House in the valley of the Saskatchewan beyond Lake Winnipeg. This was the company's first attempt to extend its influence far from its original sphere of operations on Hudson Bay, but others followed until its trading posts spanned the continent, and the corporation, entrenched upon the Pacific, ruled an empire of more than two million square miles.

The combined Nelson-Saskatchewan system, a unit broken

only by Lake Winnipeg, is 1660 miles long. Its drainage basin ranks among the leading half dozen in North America. But in the size and number of the lakes which are woven into the pattern of its intricate waterways, it yields to no other river anywhere, save only the St. Lawrence, the Mackenzie, and the Nile.

DWINDLING LAKE WINNIPEG

In the glacial age a vast lake which geologists call Agassiz overspread much territory in Minnesota, the Dakotas, and the Canadian provinces of Manitoba and Saskatchewan. Its area, estimated at 110,000 square miles, exceeded that of all five of the present Great Lakes. Tyrell, tracing its outline, found beaches carved on Duck Mountain in Manitoba at an elevation of 1365 feet above the sea, which suggested not only local up-tilting of surface, but a gradual rise of the entire region with a resultant draining away of surface waters.

Originally this inland sea emptied into the Mississippi, but as the Keewatin icecap retreated, it turned eastward to contribute the surplus of many brimming rivers through the wide channel of the Nelson into Hudson Bay.

Lakes literally by the thousand survive as dwindling relics of Agassiz. Three of them, Winnipeg, Winnipegosis, and Manitoba, rank among the world's largest, while a fourth, the Lake of the Woods, is so close to the border line that it warrants inclusion in that select list.

Pierre Radisson heard of Lake Winnipeg while scouting on the shores of Hudson Bay. When wandering Indians told him of a vast water to the westward where tides "ebbed and flowed" the credulous Frenchman concluded it must be an indentation of the Great South Sea on the route to the Indies.

Early chronicles are sketchy and incomplete. Records show that on June 12, 1690, a hardy adventurer named Henry Kelsey left York Factory, made his way up the Hayes River, and probably followed the route to the northern end of Lake Winnipeg. Thence he proceeded up the Sasketchewan, perhaps on portage between Cedar Lake and Winnipegosis.

Better authenticated is the story of Anthony Hendry, in company employ, who volunteered in 1754 to join a party of Assiniboine Indians on an expedition into this little known region. His journal, though crude and fragmentary, contains graphic entries. On one occasion he noted, "The mosquitoes are intolerable," a correct appraisal of those stinging pests from pool and muskeg. Crossing the northern sector of Lake Winnipeg in a canoe, he seems to have been the first white man to winter in the wilderness beyond. Among other incidents, he wrote, "two young men were miserably wounded by a grizzly bear." One he thought might recover, but was not sanguine about the other, whose "arm was torn from his body, one eye gouged out and his stomach ripped open." Penetrating into the great plains, Hendry encountered parties of Blackfeet Indians mounted on horses. Pompous Hudson's Bay officials, however, greeted this report with guffaws of mirth, for well they knew that Indians traveled only on foot or by canoe.

Lake Winnipeg extends roughly north and south for 260 miles. Its lower end is restricted by wooded peninsulas and innumerable islands, but toward the north it broadens out to a width of 60 miles. Its area, variously given, ranges from 8555 to 9390 square miles, the latter figure from the Canadian Cyclopedia for 1936.

Winnipeg is derived from two words in the Cree language —*Win* [murky], and *Nipy* [water]. The bottom is heavily silted and while the maximum depth is 70 feet, shallows of 12 or 15 are much more prevalent. This, no doubt, gave rise to the fabled tides, when strong winds that churned the bottom piled up the waters on one shore to expose mud flats on the other.

The largest of the numerous islands is Reindeer, with an area of 70 square miles, although Big Island is 60. Many streams flow into the lake, among them the Berens, the Poplar, and the Bloodveins. Still larger is the Red River of the North which forms the boundary between North Dakota and Minnesota, and the Winnipeg, bearing the overflow from the Lake of the Woods. Most important of all, however, is the Saskatchewan. Sweeping across the mid-continental plain from the Rockies, this great river, spreading out into Cedar Lake but a few miles to the west, enters Lake Winnipeg at Grand Rapids near its widest part.

The Nelson emerges from the lake at the northeastern corner. As the elevation is here 710 feet, that current goes foaming across the Canadian Shield down a series of rapids to the sea.

The region has a romantic setting. Here traders of the Hudson's Bay Company encountered equally daring adventurers from Three Rivers and Montreal. Against the British monopoly various independent groups organized in 1778 as the Northwest Company. Alexander Mackenzie represented one of these groups. As the wilderness recognized no law save that of craft or force, keen rivalries sometimes culminated in bloodshed.

The Hudson's Bay Company, however, determined not only to maintain but to extend its conquests. Among other outposts, Norway House was built on an island of 772 acres, opening on Playgreen Lake, which connects with the main body of Winnipeg and the Nelson River. This became a famous center for the construction of the so-called York boats, those clumsy little ships, broad of beam and with shallow draft, equipped with a single mast and sail, that bore costly freight through a maze of lakes and rivers.

In 1821 the Northwest Company merged with the Hudson's Bay, which continued to exert a shadowy control over much of the continent until October 1869. Then the Canadian government bought out the stockholders and took over the manifold functions controlled so long by individuals. The era of exploration had yielded at last to the era of development. But for nearly two centuries this organization, privately financed like the East India Company, and supervised only casually by the Crown, had played a spectacular role in the drama of empire building.

MARSHY WINNIPEGOSIS AND MANITOBA

Some distance to the west of Winnipeg lie two other lakes united with it and with each other in a loose-knit unity. All are dwindling remnants of Agassiz.

The larger and more northerly is called Winnipegosis, or Little Winnipeg. It is not so little, either, for its dimensions, 122 miles by an average width of about 17, give it an area, exclusive of islands, of 2086 square miles.

In most respects it is a minor edition of Winnipeg. Its shore lines are even more confused and formless, its innumerable wooded recesses more inaccessible. Its greatest depth is only 38 feet, while wild moose wade readily across many of its shallows. Through a veritable maze of bays and islands it empties into another similar and somewhat smaller lake to the south which is known as Manitoba. This is about 120 miles long and covers 1711 square miles. Its name, which means in the Indian dialect "Country of the Prairie Water," is highly descriptive. Its surplus contents drain into Lake Winnipeg.

Manitoba was discovered in 1739 by that notable adventurer, La Vérendrye, whose career is more intimately connected with the Lake of the Woods.

The breaking up of the super lake which once united Winnipeg, Winnipegosis, and Manitoba is still proceeding rapidly. Not far in the future, as geologists reckon time, these three will subdivide again and yet again in that slow but inevitable drying-out process which changes them eventually into vast marshes, the breeding grounds for innumerable migratory birds.

The region which they occupy, where Indians, half-breeds, and Europeans so long battled the wilderness and one another, is yielding to the progress of civilization. Mining and lumbering interests invade territory once given over exclusively to hunting and trapping; stock raising follows, then agriculture claims the fertile, silted bottom of dying Agassiz. Nor is the passing of these imposing bodies of water a landscape tragedy. Most of the world, to be sure, needs more lakes, but Canada has too many. And the wilderness will be improved by mopping up such excess moisture from the Ice Age.

THE LAKE OF THE WOODS

On the international boundary between Minnesota and Manitoba lies that lonely body of water known as the Lake of the Woods. With its many bays and islands, it fills another depression in ancient Agassiz, and together with the three larger Canadian lakes already noted forms a cluster in the Saskatchewan-Nelson system.

The lake was discovered by Jacques de Noyon, one of those daring souls who strove to expand the dominions of the king of France. In 1688, with his Indian companions, De Noyon paddled his heavily laden canoes along the southern shore of what he called, quite appropriately, the Lake of Islands.

Its real history, however, did not begin until more than forty years later with the coming of Pierre la Vérendrye, the last of the great French explorers of the New World. As a youthful soldier, he had fought bravely against the Duke of Marlborough at the battle of Malplaquet, suffered no fewer than nine wounds, and was left for dead upon the field. These wounds proved troublesome later in the bitter Minnesota winters.

La Vérendrye's father was governor of the important French settlement at Three Rivers whence De Noyon had gone adventuring, as had also those better-known explorers, La Salle, Marquette, and Jolliet. It was the younger man's mission to extend French influence in the great Northwest and arrest the expansion of the rival Hudson's Bay Company.

In 1732, after a speedy journey, he arrived at the big lake which he rechristened with its present name. Crossing to a sheltered spot on the northwestern corner, he erected a rude stockade known as Fort Charles. As described by a contemporary, "the interior of the fort is 100 feet . . . it has four bastions . . . there are also two gates at opposite sides and a watch tower, and the stakes are a double row and fifteen feet out of the ground." Father Alneau, who spent some time at the fort, mentions four rows of stakes. In any case, it was designed for survival in a region of many dangers. Inside the stockade were nine buildings stoutly constructed of logs chinked with clay that hardened almost into stone. Roofed with bark, they included a chapel and a powder magazine, for "Praise the Lord and pass the ammunition" was the imperative order of the day.

From this base of operations La Vérendrye led exploring parties far and wide and sent out others under the leadership of his three sons. One of these parties visited Lake Winnipeg and, ascending the Red River for some distance, built Fort Rouge where that stream joins the Assiniboine. The date was 1738, the purpose to cut off further incursions by the Hudson's Bay Company. From this rude settlement grew the great city

of Winnipeg. A nephew of La Vérendrye died on the expedition, the first white man to be buried in this wilderness.

Fort Charles lay on the great war road between the Cree
Indians and savage Sioux tribes farther south. Although the
French were noted for their fair dealing with the aborigines, it
was inevitable that La Vérendrye, like Champlain, should
become involved in tribal brawls. In June 1736 he dispatched
eastward a party of nineteen Frenchmen under the leadership
of his second son, Jean, accompanied by Father Alneau. Traveling in half-loaded canoes to make better speed, they camped
for the night on an island eighteen miles distant where they
were ambushed by a party of Sioux warriors and perished to
a man. La Vérendrye later found their severed heads, scalped
and laid upon beaver skins beside the bodies, and gave them
burial. The scene of this gruesome tragedy is known as Mas-
sacre Island.

In later years parties operating from Fort Charles ventured
into the country of the Mandan Indians, where they came
within sight of lofty mountains. Whether these were the
Rockies or the less remote Black Hills is still debatable.

After many years spent on the frontier, La Vérendrye
returned to Montreal in 1749, where he succumbed to sudden
illness. Fort Charles was soon deserted, fell into ruin, and was
rediscovered in 1908.

In 1820 the American Fur Company, under license from the
federal government, established a post on the lake at what is
now Warroad. The shores as well as many islands, though
popular with summer vacationists, still offer many lonely
vistas. But they no longer echo to the war whoops of painted
savages as they did in the dangerous days of La Vérendrye.

Traditions of that romantic period still linger in bits of local
folklore. There is Devil's Rock with its grotesque faces;
Wetako Island, haunt of Indian devils; and Sioux Lookout,
where warriors of that tribe were ambushed by Ojibways.

Sportsmen are attracted by the fishing, for muskellunge, lake trout, walleyed pike, and black bass abound; and by the hunting, for red deer peer furtively from spruce thickets and moose go lumbering about among the lily pads.

The Lake of the Woods has an area of 1485 square miles. Through the Winnipeg River it empties into Lake Winnipeg. By a curious quirk in geography, the jutting peninsula on the northwest corner has become the most northerly point in the continental United States. This resulted from a misunderstanding of local topography. The treaty of 1783 between the revolted colonies and the mother country delineated a boundary extending from the northwestern part of the lake due west to the Mississippi. Unfortunately, that great river lay almost due south. When this fact was recognized, a new treaty signed in 1818 agreed upon a boundary running north or south as the case might be to the 49th parallel of latitude, thence due west to the Stony (now Rocky) Mountains. The required parallel, which proved to be about twenty-six miles south, was extended to the Pacific by the treaty of 1842. And so, through a comedy of errors, that site which La Vérendrye struggled so resolutely to defend against British exploitation is still withheld from incorporation in the British Empire.

REINDEER LAKE

North of and roughly paralleling the Nelson, the Churchill River winds a thousand miles through the Canadian wilderness to empty into Hudson Bay. Of the many lakes which swell its current, the most considerable is known as Reindeer.

The length of this lake as given in the Encyclopaedia Britannica is 155 miles. Its area, according to the latest revised figures of the Canadian Hydrographic and Map Service, is

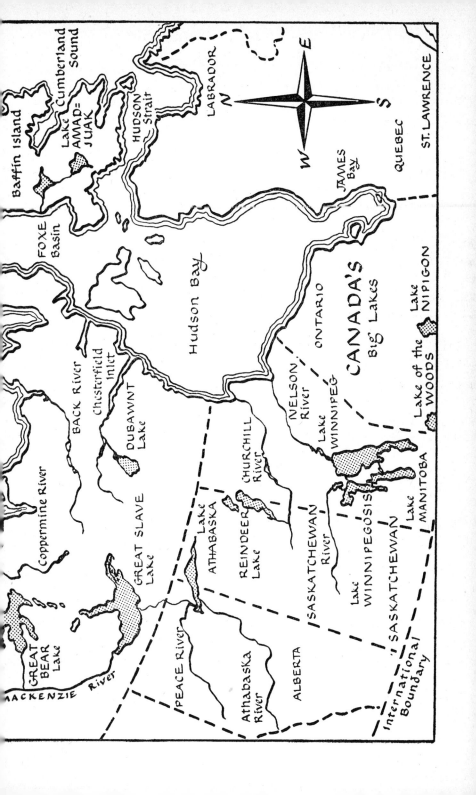

2444 square miles, which ranks it among the lesser of the world's big lakes.

It lies on the boundary between the Canadian provinces of Manitoba and Saskatchewan. The irregular shore line, 1380 miles long, is wild and varied: rocky spurs mingling with muskegs and lovely beaches with boulders and glacial till. Toward the north the terrain is sandy and barren, with scrubby growths of spruce and black birch; the southern area is better forested, mainly spruce, with some poplar not found farther north. Here the lake shores are cliffs from 200 to 400 feet high. No fewer than 3700 islands dot the coasts or stretch in chains across the surface. Many are rounded, worn smooth by glacial ice; others are covered with reindeer moss and clumps of stunted spruce.

The caribou or reindeer which once roamed the wilderness gave the lake its name. Moose sometimes frequent the shores, where the solitude is still largely unbroken. The entire region is sparsely peopled save for a small Hudson's Bay Company settlement called Brocher near the northern end of the lake, the port of a tiny twelve-ton steamer that threads its way among the maze of islands. Although soundings are meager, the lake is known to be deep. Its maximum width is about 40 miles, its elevation above sea level 1150 feet.

From the north it receives, through the Cochrane River, some of the overflow from another big lake known as Wollaston, which also empties via the Fond du Lac River into Athabaska and the Mackenzie. This queer lake illustrates the confused drainage system of the Canadian Shield, since part of its waters flow into the Arctic not far from Alaska, part into Hudson Bay.

Reindeer Lake, toward its southern extremity, narrows to four miles or less, whence it issues as the Reindeer River, flowing southward to the Churchill.

The latter river traverses a whole series of lakes, the largest,

Southern Indian, nearly a hundred miles long. Descending the uplands from one lake to another by intervening cascades, it broadens into a lagoon, some two miles wide and seven or eight long, which opens into Hudson Bay through a half-mile gap between lofty rocks.

This spot, which forms the finest harbor on the bay, is of historic interest. Here that venturesome Dane, Jens Munc, following shortly after Henry Hudson, spent a terrible winter. Open fires built on deck gave scant protection against Arctic temperatures, while scurvy took its deadly toll. In the spring Munc, the last survivor among sixty-five officers and men on board the two vessels, made what he believed was his final entry in the log, and philosophically lay down to die. At that very moment two half-famished sailors who had deserted some time before came crawling back, chewing roots and grass which alleviated their scurvy. With reviving hopes, Munc and these two men managed to work the sloop *Lamprey* out of that grisly death trap, through ice-choked straits, and home across the Atlantic. They left behind the frigate *Unicorn*, tenanted with corpses. Wondering Indians boarding her found kegs of wet powder and quite logically attempted to dry them out by building a fire. The experiment proved only too successful, as the ship and its contents disintegrated in a violent explosion.

Near this spot of ill omen the Hudson's Bay Company built its most ambitious station, Fort Prince of Wales. Flanking its walls were lofty bastions of masonry twenty to thirty feet in thickness. Forty-two cannon surmounted the parapet. It was believed to be impregnable. Then suddenly appeared French frigates under Admiral La Pérouse, who later won fame and an unknown grave exploring the Pacific, and hundreds of French soldiers emerged from the wilderness. Samuel Hearne, who was in command with only thirty-nine men, surrendered without firing a shot. The French spiked the guns and tried hard to dismantle the battlements. Matonabbee, the Indian chief who had guided Hearne to Great Slave Lake, when he found the English not invincible, committed suicide. Poor savage, he need not have been so chagrined, for empires rose and fell and rose again in those pioneering days of the Hudson's Bay Company.

Churchill is now a port of entry for a vast hinterland which seeks a nearer outlet to the sea. A railroad has been laid to distant Edmonton and the whistle of the locomotive startles a silence once broken only by the loons' weird laughter or the howl of the timber wolf. Navigation on Hudson Bay, however, is brief and the straits which connect with the Atlantic made treacherous by drifting ice. Not tamely does the lawless wilderness, so long unconquered, submit to man's control.

LITTLE-KNOWN DUBAWNT

Roughly in the longitude of Reindeer Lake, but more than three hundred miles nearer the Pole, lies one of the least known of the world's major bodies of fresh water. It is called Dubawnt, a corruption of the Indian Tobotna or "Water Shore," descriptive of a region where the two so often blend.

Dubawnt is roughly oval, its major axis extending north and south for about 65 miles, its width about 40. The Britannica gives its area as 1700 square miles, the Canadian Cyclopedia 1654. One cannot be too exact where contours are so indefinite.

The lake is an overflow of the Dubawnt River, which enters from the southwest. This curious stream has been described as made up chiefly of "lakes of great irregularity which discharge tumultuously through barrier ridges," so that only at the numerous rapids can the river be identified. This haphazard spillway emerges from the northern end of Dubawnt Lake still trending to the northeast, until it empties into Beverly, whose size would command respect anywhere else. This discharges in turn into Aberdeen Lake, a serpentine water that turns eastward and a little south to connect with Baker Lake, which goes tumbling into Chesterfield Inlet and so onward to Hudson Bay. This inlet, by the way, penetrates the continent a good hundred miles, so that ocean tides battle the fresh waters slopping over from Baker Lake.

Samuel Hearne, on his first attempt to reach the Coppermine River in 1770, crossed the Dubawnt River and made a wide circuit of the lake's western terrain, which is marked by red sandstone of ancient origin.

Dubawnt is a waif of the great barren ground. C. H. Blanchet, who flew over the region in an airplane in 1930, jotted down a few descriptive hints. The sparsely forested areas he dismissed as "scattered clumps and dwarfs." He noted "herds of caribou," while beyond stretched "the great open plains, bleak and inhospitable." Landing on a beautiful beach, he admired a vast sheet of water with its many indentations, fringing islets, and deep bays opening to the north. Yet Dubawnt is more regular in outline than most Canadian lakes, which present an almost amoeboid formlessness. Much of the surface never loses its coverlet of ice.

Beverly Lake receives the waters not only of Dubawnt but of the Thelon River, also, as it emerges from the wilderness east of Great Slave Lake. This river traverses a region described as an oasis in the great barren ground, for the soil, not entirely stripped off by the Keewatin icecap, produces a relative abundance of grass. Here in 1927 the Canadian government set apart a great tract of 15,000 square miles as a wildlife sanctuary.

In this district, which approaches within twenty-five miles of Dubawnt Lake, dwindling herds of musk oxen are protected from exploitation. This curious creature, called "ovibos," half sheep, half ox, is one of the few animals fitted to survive the long night of the Arctic winter when the thermometer sinks to 60 below and furious gales come raging down from the north. Like the woolly rhinoceros of prehistoric days, it is protected by a coat of wool beneath long hair. This not only keeps out the numbing cold, but is a protection against insect pests in summer, which drive caribou half frantic and sometimes reduce them to living skeletons. Against larger predators, the musk-ox bulls form a living ring about the calves and females which even hungry wolves dare not attack. Unfortunately Eskimos and Indians, taking no thought of the morrow, slaughtered whole herds, so that now only a few thousand survive in Greenland, Baffin Island, and the Arctic islands, while on the continent where they were once numerous they have become rare indeed.

In the Thelon Preserve, however, the Canadian census of 1928 reported 13,000 individuals. Here the ovibos blends so nicely with innumerable glacial boulders that Indians say of a distant object, "If it moves, it's a musk ox."

Stefansson, in love with his "friendly Arctic," has advocated introducing musk oxen into the uplands of Vermont, where he believes they would thrive. Whatever the future of these harmless animals, they seem safe from utter extinction in the dreary barrens beyond Dubawnt Lake.

THE BIG LAKES OF BAFFIN ISLAND

Large lakes are continental, for they require either extensive drainage basins or an integration with great rivers. Hence, although lakes do occur on islands such as Toba in Sumatra and Laguna de Bay in Luzon, only two are extensive enough for notice in this study. Strange to say, both lie within a few miles of each other in Baffin Island, that dismal terrain that stretches to the north and west above Labrador for a thousand miles or more. Discounting the semicontinent Greenland, it is the third largest island in the world, for its area of 236,000 square miles outranks Madagascar and is exceeded only by Borneo and New Guinea. The northern part is encumbered by glaciers, but the southern, broken by mountains 4000 feet high or more, broadens to a width of 350 miles in a vast undulating plain, the site of these remarkable lakes.

Although Baffin Island was discovered by Martin Frobisher in 1575, three centuries had elapsed before the first white man gazed upon these lonely bodies of water. Meanwhile, for two hundred years at least, whalers frequented Cumberland Sound, which penetrates the southeastern shore line like a tongue within twenty-four miles of the nearest of these lakes. As early as 1820 a permanent station was established on this sound by the English Captain Penny, while two stations were built later, one at Blacklead, the other at Kekerton, because the tremendous 30-foot tides kept Cumberland Sound relatively free from ice. But the sparse white population had little interest in the bleak interior.

The southernmost of Baffin's two big lakes is called by the Eskimos Amadjuak. Roughly heart-shaped, its major axis running north and south, it empties, through the short Amadjuak River, into the second big lake, lying north and west. This lake, called Nettilling, meaning "Flat Shores," is shaped somewhat like a collapsed kite. A broad but shallow river flowing almost due west carries the overflow sixty miles to desolate Foxe Basin in the Arctic. This river is the Koukjuak, though the spelling of Eskimo words is quite as variable as English in Shakespeare's day.

The German Dr. Frank Boas, sailing from Europe in 1883, first ascended the chain of lakes and short portages that led from Cumberland Sound to Nettilling. There he lived among the natives, learned their language, and studied the Silurian limestones of the region. He also traveled overland to the shores of Amadjuak.

Not long afterward, in 1885, Dr. Robert Bell, acting for the Canadian government, penetrating northward from Hudson Strait, discovered a third lake some 15 miles long called Mingo. A few miles farther on, from the top of a hill which his anerode showed was 966 feet high, he gazed out across the broad waters of Amadjuak. Some miles offshore lay an island 10 miles long that he named Victoria. The farther shore of the lake loomed mistily at a distance which he estimated at 40 miles.

From the uplands, saturated with moisture, many little streams cascaded into the lake. Grass carpeted the valleys, the meadows were bright with Arctic flowers, clumps of dwarf shrubbery dotted the hillsides. Butterflies and bumblebees flitted about, reindeer appeared in scattered bands, while on his journey Bell encountered foxes, both blue and white, and an occasional wolf. There were no trees. Baffin Island appeared to him "mountainous, rugged, bleak, and barren, a desolate waste inhabited only by a few hundred nomadic Eskimos and several isolated whaling stations."

He found the elevation of the big lake 292 feet above sea level, and thought it smaller than Nettilling, farther north, which he estimated to be 160 miles by 60.

The next inspection of record was in 1897, when a party of Eskimos visited Amadjuak on a caribou hunt, but, running out of provisions, were obliged to eat their dogs. The lake was also visited by members of the Donald MacMillan Expedition wintering on the southern shore of Baffin Island.

The first man to circumnavigate Nettilling was Crawford Noble, son of the owner of one of the whaling stations on Cumberland Sound. In 1902, with a group of Eskimos, he dragged a whaleboat up the intervening portages for a three months' hunting trip. But his interests lay in caribou and snow geese rather than in topographical measurements, though he did bring back a rough sketch map and noted some landscape features in his journal.

In 1910 the German, Bernard Hantzsch, set out to cross Baffin Island and explore its western coast. In this undertaking he succeeded at the cost of his life. Crossing Nettilling with a few Eskimos, he unearthed on its marshy western shore the jawbone of a walrus and the rib of a whale. The presence of many specimens of the hooded seal (*Phoca hispida*) also indicated a previous connection with the sea. Passing down the Koukjuak River, three miles wide and impeded with rocks and shoals, he found the seacoast swampy and seemingly but a few inches above sea level. He had proceeded northward along the shore of Foxe Basin for about a hundred miles when he was forced to make camp for the winter. No heat was available in temperatures that sank to 60 degrees below zero. The food supply was precarious and starvation imminent. Entries in his diary expressed a resigned but poignant forecast of the end. With the coming of spring, he tried to force his way back to the Koukjuak River, but, subsisting on raw flesh and weakened by privation, he sickened on the meat of a gaunt white bear, developed fever, and died. His followers buried him some miles from a little river flowing westward, which is named for him. In their simple language, "We made a nice grave of stones and it is a good place. His body cannot be disturbed by foxes or a wolf." Not even the tomb of Sir Ernest Shackleton on South Georgia Island is so forlorn or inaccessible.

In 1924 Major Burwash explored the northeastern sector of Nettilling through a perfect maze of granitic islands. The following year J. Dewey Soper, acting for the Canadian Museum, established a base on the southern shore from which he conducted extensive explorations. Ice did not disappear until late

August. He found the country to the west a vast plain sprinkled with lakes as far as the eye could see. The next year Constable Tredgold of the Northwestern Mounted Police continued the survey around the northwestern corner, a large bay called by the Eskimos Karmang, where they came in summer to hunt caribou.

Soper again visited Nettilling and made a map. In the dreary region which stretches to the southwest he located the favorite breeding ground of the shy blue goose of Canada. The land was swampy with innumerable lakes. In Foxe Basin thirty-foot tides ebbed five miles or more, revealing an interminable waste of mud flats.

Nettilling is cut by the Arctic Circle and lies in about the latitude of the upper sector of Great Bear Lake. Its dimensions, as given by the Hydrographic and Map Service of the Canadian government, are "70 miles north and south, 60 miles east and west," its area "2100 square miles." Smaller Amadjuak is given an area of 1207. The Eskimos told Soper of a third great lake beyond the present range of the white man, a story which awaits confirmation. Whatever the facts may be, Baffin Island embraces the loneliest of all big lakes.

GREAT SALT LAKE

On July 24, 1847, Brigham Young, commanding a caravan of thousands of hardy pioneers, gazed out over a broad expanse of waters shimmering in the distance and announced, "This is the place." Truly a dramatic moment in history, it marked the founding of a new state, the establishment of a new religion, in the still uncharted wilderness.

The numerous band of Latter-day Saints, commonly known as Mormons, had journeyed far from the banks of the Mississippi, where they had been subjected to grievous persecution. Resolved to seek a refuge beyond the wilderness, they had braved countless perils with fortitude. No wonder the valley of the Wasatch seemed like another Promised Land to these modern Israelites wandering in the desert. How they laid out the streets of a great city and developed a region destined to become the state of Utah is another story. But the waters which so appealed to Brigham Young hold a special interest in the study of lake formation and decline.

Great Salt Lake lies at an elevation of 4218 feet above the sea. It is the largest among a number of lakes—Utah, Sevier, and others that survive as remnants of that vaster lake called Bonneville, nearly as large as Huron, which once flooded all this region. Some 19,000 square miles in extent, it drained northward into the Columbia River. Its waters, which would have submerged the streets of Salt Lake City to a depth of a thousand feet, gradually subsided until they left no fewer than seventeen beach levels engraved on the surrounding heights. Soon the outlet no longer functioned, the region developed as an interior drainage basin, and the profound depths of Bonneville became mere saline shallows that tended to degenerate into melancholy salt marshes.

Great Salt Lake is about 75 miles long, but it is so shallow and its levels subject to such marked alterations that its boundaries are elastic to a degree. The seasonal differences determined by the influx of the Jordan, Weber, and Bear rivers and the rapidity of evaporation amount to 16 inches annually. But during the past century the lake surface has undergone changes in elevation of more than thirty feet. At its maximum it had an area of perhaps 2000 square miles. As water depths lessened to twenty-five feet, that area was reduced to about 1750; at fifteen feet it shrunk further to about 1500. Such cycles indicate a progressive decline as the season of 1936 witnessed the lowest levels yet recorded.

These extraordinary fluctuations are thought to be accompanied by a perceptible tilting in rock strata, for retreating shore lines in some quarters are offset in others by fences standing in water a mile or more from land.

The salinity of the waters has varied with their volume. An analysis by W. Blum in 1904 showed more than twice the figure obtained by Charles Smart in 1877. In general terms it may be said that recorded observations give a salinity that ranges from four to seven times that of the Atlantic. In the latter stage it approximates the density of the Dead Sea.

Gilbert has estimated that the lake contains no fewer than four hundred million tons of chlorides and thirty million tons of sulphates. No wonder swimmers find a disconcerting buoyancy which makes sinking impossible. The shores are sandy, the lake bottom mainly crusted with salt, soda, and gypsum.

From the north a mountainous peninsula projects far into the lake. Of the several islands Fremont and Antelope are the most considerable. Lake depths are nowhere very great, but the central trough, about 25 miles wide, from northwest to southeast shows numerous soundings of 40 feet with a maximum of 60. Across one shallow sector the artificial cut-off of the Union Pacific Railroad stretches for twenty-seven miles.

The aquatic life which once abounded in Lake Bonneville has dwindled to a few species of algae, some degenerate brine shrimp, and the larval forms of certain insects. Water temperatures range from 85 degrees in August to 25 in February. In winter sodium sulphate is precipitated, only to dissolve again in summer.

The mineral content is a considerable source of wealth. Brine is pumped into artificial ponds, where the salt is deposited by evaporation, and then refined. Glauber's salt is also of commercial importance.

The dry bed of ancient Bonneville is generally fertile where water is available. An annual rainfall ranging from 12 to 20 inches is supplemented by streams from the Wasatch Mountains which culminate in peaks over 12,000 feet high. The so-called Salt Lake Oasis, where irrigation is extensive, covers 680 square miles.

Great Salt Lake was mentioned by Baron de Lahontan in 1689, although he gained his information from Indians. The famous scout, Jim Bridger, seems to have been the first white man to see the lake—the year, 1824. Frémont, in 1845, presented a fairly accurate description.

Among neighboring cities Ogden and Salt Lake City are the largest. In the latter metropolis, with its broad streets and imposing temple dedicated to the faith which he professed, Brigham Young, were he alive today, would find that the vision which so inspired him a century ago had become a reality. This was, indeed, "the place."

LAKE NICARAGUA AND ITS FUTURE

Perhaps no other big lake has such alluring prospects as Nicaragua. For it is the dream of the coastal cities which drowse in Spanish somnolence that the long-projected interocean canal will someday emerge from survey map and blueprint to transform their lake into one of the major highways of the world.

Nicaragua lies in the republic of that name, its western shore but sixteen miles from the Pacific, its eastern somewhat more distant from the Atlantic. One hundred and ten miles long and 45 in width, its area is 3089. Once it was even more extensive, uniting with Lake Managua, 38 miles by 16, which also fills part of the valley. This valley, a former gulf of the Pacific, was dammed off by volcanic upheaval and its imprisoned waters changed from salt to fresh. Managua, higher by fifteen feet, now drains into Nicaragua through the Tipitapa River, an eccentric stream whose frequent stretches of dry bed overlie subterranean channels.

Both lakes are the handiwork of the volcanoes. Grim cones not only frown from the hinterland but encroach upon the shore line and emerge as islands from the lake floor. Several are still smoldering, led by fire-breathing Momotombo. Two volcanoes, Concepcion and Madera, have coalesced to form Ometepe Island, 20 miles long, which lies halfway up Lake Nicaragua's western shore. Concepcion erupted in 1883 and has shown signs of more recent truculence. Near this island the lake reaches its greatest depth, about 200 feet. Smaller islets are so beautiful in the morning light that the natives call them "diamonds."

Dead craters flooded with tropic rains hold tiny lakelets of their own. One of the loveliest is Asososca, a jade-green gem set in crumbling lava. Lake Apoya, in another crater, is a vivid blue, while from the dead heart of Coseguina the waters reflect the skies in shades of sapphire, emerald, and muddy brown. When this lake bed was excavated by the terrific explosion of 1835, the sound was heard at Bogota, eleven hundred miles away.

Nicaragua reveals its oceanic origin in such marine life as sharks, sawfish, and that giant of the herring family, the tarpon. Sharks, acclimated to its fresh waters, have evolved a unique species, *Eulamia nicaraguensis*, found nowhere else. These unwelcome intruders, which may weigh two hundred pounds or more, are true man-eaters, for scarcely a season passes that some swimmer does not fall victim to their voracity. Two species of sawfish also occur, one producing specimens weighing over seven hundred pounds.

Nicaragua empties into the Caribbean through the crooked San Juan River, which is much interrupted by sand bars and rapids, particularly at El Castillo, where a portage is necessary. Otherwise small steamers have long navigated its 130-mile length, which traverses the steaming lowlands to the seaport at Greytown. There, in 1938, the rainfall registered 334 inches!

The Indians called their big lake Cocibolca, which the Spaniards changed in honor of Nicarao, a friendly chief. The explorer De Avila, commissioned by the Crown to solve the secret of the isthmus, heard from the natives of a vast Mare Dulce or fresh-water sea, far to the north. Approaching from the Pacific, he discovered the lake in 1529, while the outlet through the San Juan was explored from 1531–34.

The native villages which lined the shores soon gave way to Spanish cities, while what is now the United States and Canada remained unbroken wilderness.

Nicaragua awoke to the possibilities of world commerce in the days of the California gold rush. Some hardy forty-niners trekked across the continent through deserts beset by hostile Indians. Less hazardous was the long sea voyage around Cape Horn, when clipper ships made record voyages against Antarctic gales. Still more popular was the voyage to Greytown, then up the San Juan River, across the lake, and by stage coach to the Pacific, with the easy last lap to San Francisco by sea. Commodore Vanderbilt, alert to transportation profits, developed this route and controlled both river steamers and stagecoaches. Here, too, came that romantic adventurer, William Walker, arch Southerner and proslavery partisan, who had edited a San Francisco paper. Observing richer opportunities than washing gold in California, he seized control of the local government and made himself dictator. In such a coup a rank outsider was about as secure as though seated on the rim of a Nicaraguan volcano. Still, Walker for several years maintained his headquarters at Granada on the lake beneath the menacing crest of Mount Mombacho, and might have prolonged his tenure of office had not the crusty commodore, whom he had offended, supplied his enemies with firearms. As it was, he became embroiled with neighboring "republics" and met the fate of most soldiers of fortune when he was executed in Honduras in 1860.

Lake Nicaragua's strategic position between two oceans was recognized more than three centuries ago. As far back as 1544 the citizens of Granada petitioned the Spanish sovereign for fifty husky Negroes to deepen the channel of the San Juan in order to permit readier access to the sea. For a time the comparative merits of Nicaragua were weighed against those of Panama, nor have proponents of the northern route ceased to champion theirs as the better choice. In 1914 the United States Government paid $3,000,000 to Nicaragua for a perpetual option on a canal route, with the right to establish and maintain suitable defenses.

A survey of this proposed route was made and filed for future reference. It follows the San Juan River, thence across the lake by a long diagonal, and through the lowest, narrowest land wall to the Pacific. With approaches the distance is 173 miles. Although lake depths are generally ample, a channel would have to be dredged through the soft mud along the eastern shore for 14 miles. Three locks at each end of the lake route would be required to offset the difference of 105 feet in sea and lake levels. Even the possible effect of future volcanic disturbance on these locks has been forecast by competent engineers.

During the late war it became apparent that interocean traffic had well-nigh outgrown the Panama Canal. Moreover, locks designed for all conceivable requirements barely permitted the entry of the largest airplane carriers. In a world of such violent change, where the expenditure of billions has become a commonplace, a new and shorter seaway from our eastern to our western coasts may be a sound investment. It would develop a region of vast potential resources, enhance friendly relations with neighboring governments to the south, and might prove invaluable should an atomic bomb or even an 8-ton blockbuster ever drop "inadvertently" upon the locks of Panama.

South American Lakes

FABLED TITICACA

Loftiest of the world's big lakes is Titicaca. Its wind-tormented surface, 12,507 feet above the neighboring Pacific, fills the deeper recesses of an interior basin thrust skyward for nearly two and a half miles by vast upheavals, and barred from the outside world by the still loftier Andes. Nor is the mighty pageant ended, for there is reason to believe that the valley was lower even within historic time and that the upward surging of the earth crust is still progressing.

Titicaca forms part of the boundary between Bolivia and Peru. One hundred and twenty-five miles long with an extreme width of 41, it covers approximately 3200 square miles. Along the eastern shore a deep trough shows soundings of 892 feet. On the whole, however, the lake averages little more than a hundred, and steamers sometimes run aground on submerged mudbanks.

The coast line, in places, is abrupt, in others gently sloping. Along the western shore the scarp is concealed by vast lava flows from distant volcanoes, long dormant or extinct, which notch the sky line at heights of twenty thousand feet or more. Elsewhere the shores are low and swampy, lush with rank vegetation, where giant tortora reeds or bulrushes higher than a man's head provide not only fodder for cattle but materials for baskets, mats, and roofing thatch. Still stranger is their use in the picturesque reed boats or balsas, which have navigated Titicaca from immemorial times. Propelled by sails of finer reeds, these odd craft, which commonly last about two years, must be dried out occasionally to avoid becoming water-logged.

Titicaca's waters are icy cold, yet they never freeze. In the spring, when melted snows pour down from the Andes, they may rise five or six feet. Mainly fresh, they become brackish in the shallows during the dry season. They swarm with fish, while the marshy lowlands are the haunt of innumerable aquatic birds. Into their peaceful breeding grounds a morose condor sometimes swoops down from distant heights, causing general havoc.

Although a branch of the Beni River, one of the tributaries of the Amazon, approaches within less than ten miles of Titicaca, there is no evidence that the valley has ever had an outlet. The lake was once much larger, however, extending southeastward to embrace several lesser lakes, intensely saline, into which it empties by the shallow Desaguadero River. These lakes, mere films of water scarcely four feet deep and nowhere more than thirteen, overflow in turn into dismal salt swamps to evaporate or be sucked up by the thirsty earth. The presence of former coastal towns now some miles inland bears witness to subsiding levels.

The western portion of the lake valley is pastoral. There wild llamas, alpacas, and vicuñas once roamed in vast herds. Although the altitude would seem to preclude a flourishing agriculture, barley and other vegetables ripen. Here was the original home of quinoa, a grain peculiar to Peru, and here flourished those misshapen tubers from which some nameless Indian Burbank developed the potato, now a staple food crop of the world.

Titicaca is almost bisected by two approaching rocky peninsulas and their outlying shoals. Several islands dot its surface, the largest, Isla del Sol, or Island of the Sun, covered with cyclopean ruins of temples, palaces, and perhaps fortresses. The neighboring Island of the Moon is also the site of carved and fitted stonework which has intrigued archaeologists since the days of the Spanish Conquest. For this isolated valley is the traditional cradle of the Inca race, those masterful builders who swept down from the mountains to conquer a coastal empire two thousand miles long and create a splendid civilization peculiar to the New World. Perhaps no other lake is so interwoven with the history of an important people.

A more recent monument marks another islet in memory of James Orton, an explorer who died while crossing Titicaca in 1876 and is buried in this lonely but appropriate spot.

The lake has always been an important trade center. From its shores well-trodden paths lead through the gorges of the Andes, where laden llamas or sweating human porters, energized by chewing coca leaves, the basis of cocaine, once bore gold and silver to adorn the palaces of the emperor or the temples of the sun. Now lake steamers introduce a discordant note among archaic balsas as they speed to and fro with the diversified commerce of an area rich in mineral and other wealth. Ambitious plans have even been drawn for tunneling off surplus waters to supply gigantic hydroelectric plants, as science finds the storied region an inviting field.

Someday this isolated body of water, brooding in its sequestered valley, may turn from memories of vanished greatness to new prominence among the important lakes of the future.

MARACAIBO—LAKE OR LAGOON?

The southern shore line of the Caribbean is pierced by a deep indentation—the Gulf of Maracaibo. At its head this narrowing tongue of sea penetrates still farther inland through a tortuous channel thirty-five miles long to connect with that vast sheet of mingled fresh and brackish water known as Lake Maracaibo.

There is some doubt whether this landlocked pocket should be considered a lake at all. It does not quite fulfill Webster's definition, "a considerable *inland* body of standing water," for ocean tides seep through its shallow outlet. The Encyclopaedia Britannica prefers to class it as a lagoon or inlet from the sea. Though originally an ocean gulf, it is now almost isolated and seems destined to become fresh water. Hence it should perhaps be recognized as a lake in process of formation.

Roughly ovate in form, Maracaibo is nearly 100 miles in length with an extreme width of about 60. The outlet to the sea is broad—from 4 to 10 miles—and shallow, as it breaks up into no fewer than thirteen passageways interspersed with sand bars and low-lying islands. Even the main ship channel has a depth of only 7 feet at low water.

Near the sea the lake is relatively shoal and brackish, due to the infiltration of salt water. Farther inland it deepens to 60 feet or more, with extreme soundings of over 100, so that it is readily navigable by steamers. The waters also become fresh, diluted by dozens of streams that flow down from the lofty hinterland. At least three of these streams are navigable for some distance, providing natural arteries of commerce into the rich and still undeveloped interior.

Not far from the southern shore the mountains rear a formidable barrier of peaks from 14,000 to 15,000 feet high. On their seaward slopes the annual precipitation exceeds 86 inches, while that of the entire lake basin is not much under 70. This abundant rainfall and the influx of so many streams, combined with the gradual silting up of the broad exit, is turning Maracaibo into a true lake.

A belt of fertile territory with dense forests intervenes between the mountains and the southern shore line. Among other tropic woods are ebony, mahogany, and the singular árbol de leche, whose sap resembles thickened milk and is widely used as such.

From the interior come cocoa, coffee, sugar, quinine, dyewoods, hides, and many other commodities, for the lake and its numerous tributaries are a natural waterway for commerce.

Toward the west the coastal strip is broken by savannahs and smaller lakes separated from the main body and now become fresh water. Farther north extensive salt pans appear as relics of the sea. Here the climate is semiarid, although goat farms and cattle ranches provide the basis of a growing industry. Maracaibo also abounds with fish and fleets of fishing boats enliven waters little troubled save by tropic thundershowers.

The northeastern shores present a curious picture. Here huge oil derricks advance far from land, for rich petroleum deposits underlie much of the lake bottom. Here also one finds a novel division among foreign concessions. The Shell Oil Company controls the shore rights with numerous wells and storage tanks. The Gulf Oil Company pre-empts the shallows to a depth of 15 feet, with borings that penetrate oil-bearing strata. In the deeper waters beyond, which fall under the jurisdiction of a subsidiary of the Standard Oil Company of New Jersey, some of the most productive wells in the area delve through 35 feet of water. Just how much of Maracaibo's bed may prove productive is undetermined.

Coal seams also occur in the neighborhood, for this region, where Spanish adventurers risked their lives for gold, seems to be a storehouse of more fabulous riches.

The metropolis is Maracaibo, whose population long since passed the 100,000 mark. Situated some miles from the northern shore, it guards the exit to the sea.

The Indian name for the lake was Coquibacoa. The first Spaniard who visited its beaches was Alonso de Ojeda, one of the most indefatigable of the conquistadors. Endowed by the Crown with vast estates on the mainland of South America, he set out to investigate. Approaching the lake, he observed an Indian village set upon stakes in the shallow water, like the prehistoric lake dwellings of Switzerland. This reminded him of Venice, so he called the district Venezuela or Little Venice, a name now appropriated by the entire country.

With characteristic brutality Ojeda attacked one of these aquatic towns but learned to his sorrow that the natives held a potent defensive weapon in their poisoned arrows. Several Spaniards fell beneath these deadly missiles, and Ojeda himself was glad to escape, exhausted, to the seacoast, where his companions rescued him as he lay collapsed across the roots of a giant mango tree.

Maracaibo is the stage for a strange phenomenon. Shortly after sunset the dark background of mountains is illuminated by a continuous play of lightning, lasting until dawn, so vivid that they are visible from sea. The cause has been ascribed to electric sparks generated when warm air rising from the lake surface contacts chill currents from the mountains. Whatever the explanation, this nightly display of fiery flickerings is a spectacle which no other lake can rival.

X

Lakes and Civilization

MOUNTAIN LAKES

In those earth convulsions in which mountains emerged from the upsurging crust, a multitude of lakes were born. They are natural pockets for collecting rains or melted snows, formed when rock strata buckled or were dislocated by cracks or faults. Many were produced by glaciers which gouged out the solid rock or heaped up dams of detritus. Occasionally the glacier was its own obstruction and the barrier a mere wall of ice. Lake Castain in Alaska and Märjelen in the Alps are examples to remind us of that chill age when continental ice fields blocked off such inland seas as Agassiz and Ojibway in North America.

Geologists prefer to tabulate mountain lakes in various categories, but they are created by warpings or cracks in the earth crust, by volcanic action, already dealt with elsewhere, or by glacial erosion or moraine.

A rarer type, however, is caused by landslides which dam up mountain streams. In 1914 Sir Aurel Stein, exploring Central Asia, observed such a slide on the edge of the Pamirs, which had imprisoned a river and created a lake fifteen miles long. The waters, slowly rising, might remain impounded for many centuries. A number of such lakes occur in northeastern California.

Mountain lakes are usually either long and lenticular, filling drowned valleys, or irregular, occupying deep furrows around the flanks of mountains. They are often of great depth. Loch

Morar in western Scotland is 1017 feet deep; Maggiore in northern Italy, 1220; and Como in the same jumbled terrain, 1358. This is deeper than Lake Superior. Como was long considered the deepest lake in Europe, But K. M. Strom discovered soundings of 1686 feet in Hornindalsvatn, while at least three other Norwegian lakes are deeper than Como.

Mountain lakes frequently lie far above sea level. Tahoe, on the border between California and Nevada, has an elevation of 6275 feet. Famed for its beauty, this charming bit of water, 20 miles long by 12 broad, and 1650 feet deep, has forced an outlet through the Truckee River.

North of Bhutan, in the shadow of gigantic Kalhakangri, 24,700 feet high, is Lake Pomo Pso, some 20 miles long. M. Bailey decided it was at least 16,000 feet above sea level, while Askal Chin, in the same disturbed terrain of tableland and mountain peak, is said to lie at an elevation of 16,600 feet, or well over three miles.

The highest lake in the world is undetermined. But it doubtless reflects a bit of blue sky somewhere amid the formidable gorges of the Himalaya or Karakorum ranges.

Best known of mountain lakes is Geneva, the largest lake in Central Europe, which defines part of the border between France and Switzerland. Formed by a spreading out of the river Rhone as it flows through a deep valley, it is roughly lens-shaped, 39 miles long by 8½ broad, with an area of 225 square miles. Its greatest depth is 1015 feet. The surroundings are magnificent, with Mount Blanc, highest of the Alps, looming not many miles distant.

Here those curious tremors known as seiches were first observed in 1730 by the Swiss engineer De Duillier, and made the theme of exhaustive research by Professor Forel, father of limnology, the scientific study of lakes. These strange pulsations, suggesting, yet so unlike, the tides, maintain a regular schedule, one following the long, the other the transverse axis.

In October 1841 the water at one end of the lake rose over six
feet. Since that time these mysterious movements have been
observed elsewhere, even in partially enclosed arms of the sea.
One in Lake Erie seems to follow a cycle of more than fifteen
hours, another in a small pond has been timed in fourteen
seconds. Seiches are still a puzzle, though they have been
ascribed to variations in atmospheric pressure complicated by
wind action.

Geneva, known to the Romans as Lacus Lemanus, is sometimes called Lake Leman. It has repeatedly offered sanctuary
to men of genius who fled from irksome restrictions or actual
persecution elsewhere. Here, among others, Voltaire, the
stormy petrel of French pre-Revolutionary ideas, defied the
power of French monarchs and held almost regal court. Here
John Calvin forged the framework of the Presbyterian faith,
secure from the wrath of Rome. But there were darker shadows, too, religious and political tyranny, evidenced by that
gloomy dungeon immortalized by Lord Byron in *The Prisoner
of Chillon*. Surely few lakes have had a stranger history than
this blue reservoir of troubled waters in its setting of snowy
mountains.

PREHISTORIC LAKE DWELLERS

Primitive man appreciated his lakes. He turned to them instinc-
tively, not for their scenic beauties, but for more elemental
reasons, as desirable homesites. Nor did he erect his shelters in
some sequestered nook, but out over placid waters on plat-
forms fashioned by the crudest of tools and constructed with
incredible labor.

His reasoning, so far as we can follow it, seems logical
enough. A lake offered security in an age whose only law was

that of fang and claw and bludgeon. It was both a moat against his enemies and an unfailing source of supply. Seated under his own "vine and fig tree," he could dip up water for his daily needs or catch fish for breakfast without resorting to some brook where savage beasts or still more savage fellow humans might ambush him. All about were air and sunlight and that freedom which he could never know in caves or gloomy forests.

From a timid semianimal lurking in clefts of the rock or under rude tree shelters, he became a builder who depended upon his brain as well as his hands. He also learned that communal enterprise could develop projects beyond the limits of his single strength and skill. With the confidence that came from triumph over his surroundings, there doubtless awoke within him the first rude joy of creative effort.

We may look upon such lake settlements as the forerunners of more pretentious cities, where man first learned to dwell in harmony with his neighbors and establish the foundations of modern society. From his dwelling on stakes he gazed out over wider horizons, observed the sky above as well as the earth beneath, and began that conquest of nature which has never ceased. We might even speculate with a fine show of plausibility that in such primitive villages the germs of human culture were implanted, and that lakes were the very cradles of civilization.

Lake villages set upon piles are pictured in Assyrian bas-reliefs. Children seem to have been tethered by the feet to prevent their falling into the water, and domesticated cattle were fed, in part at least, on fish.

Two firsthand descriptions of such villages have come down to us from the fifth century B.C. Hippocrates tells us how the people of the Phasis district on the eastern coasts of the Black Sea erected rude structures of timber and reeds amid their inundated marshes, and fashioned boats from a single tree trunk. Herodotus gives a clearer picture of such a village in Lake Prasias in Thrace. "There is," he wrote, "set in the midst of the lake a platform made fast on tall poles whereto one bridge gives a narrow passage to the land. The piles which support the platform were set there in old times by all the people working together." Such a settlement could be readily defended as the inhabitants dared defy even the army of Darius, when he marched against the Scythians.

In Europe lake villages have been traced from the British Isles to Russia. Rudest of all, perhaps, were the Irish crannogs, artificial islets made of brush or sod confined by stakes and stones. As early as 1857 no fewer than forty-six of these communal centers had been identified. Similar structures, hardly superior in workmanship to those of beavers, have been found in the lochs of Scotland. An English village revealed stakes sharpened by fire and driven into the mud from which were unearthed many rude implements along with the bones of *Bos primogenius*, the huge, extinct ox of prehistoric forests.

Other European lakes show more pretentious settlements, but lake culture, if we may call it such, reached its peak in Switzerland and the neighboring waters of Italy and France. More than two hundred lake villages have been discovered there, a remarkable survival when we consider that their antiquity is measured not in seasons or in centuries, but in thousands of years.

For a long time Swiss fishermen had told stories of nets torn on submerged tree stumps. It was not, however, until the winter of 1853–54 that droughts, which lowered lake surfaces to unprecedented levels, revealed these drowned woodlands as the remains of prehistoric villages.

The great drought of 1920–21 also aided explorations, so that archaeologists may now reconstruct the life and customs of the period.

There is no evidence that these lake dwellers were a peculiar race; they merely recognized the superiority of an aquatic environment. The most ancient villages, which date back to Neolithic times, are thought to be at least seven thousand years old. As the sole available tools were of stone or staghorn, the builders often sharpened the piles by fire. They wore ornaments rimmed from human skulls!

As mankind slowly advanced, his relics became more numerous and of improved workmanship. They also reveal the first crude refinements of civilization: skates made of staghorn, saws with flint teeth fixed in wood by asphalt; necklaces fashioned from bear's teeth. The Age of Bronze ushered in a new world of mechanical equipment. A few later villages even witnessed the introduction of iron implements, for they were still occupied in the days of Julius Caesar.

Among the mass of accumulated relics fishhooks, harpoons, and rude nets show the prominence of fish on the bill of fare. Many other food items have been recovered from baskets or blackened earthenware pots, even charred remnants of coarse bread perfectly preserved. Wheat, barley, beans, and other seeds revealed some progress in agriculture; while mingled with the remains of wild fruits, acorns, and nuts were the bones of European bison, deer, sheep, swine, goats, domestic cattle, and many smaller animals.

The weaving art which began with fishnets and mats woven from rushes showed notable improvement. Threads were spun from flax and wool, and the manufacture of cloth began. Tools became complex and numerous, earthenware pottery relatively common and of improved design. Copper rings have been recovered which are believed to be among our oldest specimens of money.

Preserved in chill waters, ancient piling became endowed with something akin to immortality. The piles, commonly ten feet long and from four to eight inches in diameter, were driven for three or four feet into the bottom sand or mud. For this purpose they were sharpened at one end either by axes or, in more ancient examples, by fire. On rocky bottom they were fixed in position by heaping stones about them. We catch a glimpse of the stupendous labor involved when we learn that the village known as Wangen employed no fewer than 50,000 piles, while Bodman, on Lake Constance, 1343 feet long by 163 feet wide, was supported on 61,500.

Crosspieces were lashed to the tops of the piling and over them unbarked poles laid down, or in later improvements very rough planking. Over this foundation clay was spread to give a firm, smooth surface.

In his dwelling houses primitive man evolved a rude architecture which combined simplicity with utility. The homes of the more aristocratic lake dwellers were sometimes commodious. One has been observed 70 feet long by 50 feet wide. Perhaps it served as a communal center. A well-preserved dwelling is 33 by 23 feet, divided into compartments, with walls of split tree trunks. Often the walls were of wattle work, plastered with clay. The fireplace was of baked clay, the roof thatched with rushes, straw, or bark. In some villages the houses stood about three feet apart. Stables apparently accommodated cattle.

Among the twenty-four villages so far discovered in Lake Geneva, the one known as Norges was 1200 feet long by 150 wide. Its population has been estimated at 1200 persons. Evidently the site was a popular one, for successive layers show that the original village was constructed in the Stone Age, a successor when stone implements were supplemented with those of copper, and a third built during the Age of Bronze.

Over fifty settlements have been observed in Lake Bienne. One, called Sutz, which covered six acres, gained access to the shore by a passageway 40 feet wide and 300 feet long. Another, known as Robenhausen, in what was formerly the bed of Lake Pfäffikon, was connected with the shore by a bridge-like affair more than half a mile long. Here the piles, appearing in three layers of sediment, number 100,000!

A few villages were evidently islands accessible only by canoe. One canoe has been discovered thirty feet in length loaded with stones to be placed about the piling. Another, hollowed from a single huge tree, was 43 feet long and 4 feet 4 inches wide!

It has been conjectured that the more elaborate villages were erected during a period of prolonged drought which may have continued for a thousand years or more and reduced lake surfaces far below their present levels. The majority of relics, which number many thousands, seem to date back to the Stone Age.

Aquatic dwellings still survive in various parts of the world: among certain African tribes, the Dyaks of Borneo, and in many other places. Cool and airy, they have much to commend them. Such dwellings in Lake Maracaibo, as already noted, gave the name Venezuela or Little Venice to a South American republic. But it was only in prehistoric times that entire peoples, driven by dread of the wilderness, sought shelter and the opportunity to develop a crude but definite culture amid friendly lakes.

SCENIC LAKES

No landscape seems complete without a glimpse of water. Whether this be a lake shore, a winding stream, or a bit of the sea is perhaps debatable. The sea suggests boundless power and turmoil, the stream a motion gentle but tireless, the lake serenity and calm.

Wooded shores or gently rolling slopes enhance lacustrine beauty, as do rocky islets; but a background of mountains is perhaps the perfect setting. From scenes mirrored at their base, the imagination ascends such distant heights to lose itself amid the clouds.

Among the hundreds of thousands of lakes that adorn the continents and islands of the world, a multitude have been preferred by universal acclaim as scenic gems. Such is Chocorua, beloved by countless tourists of New England. In the light of the full moon, both lake and mountain appear like a ghostly silver print. And those fortunate enough to observe Lake George in New York, when its waters dissolve the gold and bronze and crimson of autumn foliage from mountainous shores and islands, have been privileged to gaze across the very threshold of fairyland.

Still grander are Lake Louise in Canada or Tahoe in California-Nevada, while Como and Maggiore, with sun-bathed Italy in the foreground and the icy peaks of the Alps in the background, have been world-famous for centuries.

Arguments over the most beautiful of lakes are endless and no doubt futile also. Yet travelers have not hesitated to express decided opinions. Sir Frank Younghusband, exploring the forbidden kingdom of Tibet, found his ultimate quest of beauty in barbaric Yamdok Tso, "the Turquoise Lake." Its name was appropriate, although he observed its colors melt through endless shades of violet, blue, and green. Thirty-five miles across, this lake almost surrounds a mountainous peninsula like a watery girdle. Though lying at an elevation of 13,800 feet, its colorful surface mirrors the peaks of the distant Himalayas with less gigantic but still imposing heights on every side. A few miles to the north winds the great river Brahmaputra, searching for the gorges which give it escape to the plains of India and the sea. Lhasa, home of the Living Buddha, with his thousands of monks, is scarcely fifty miles distant. Amid such surroundings fancy has placed the Shangri-La of untroubled contemplation, shut off from the outer world.

Far different is Bangweulu in Central Africa. Yet the English traveler, Weatherley, found its mysterious lagoons, leading into a maze of papyrus swamp fringed with lotus blossoms, a scene of savage but almost unbelievable loveliness.

Surroundings far more commonplace have invested many a bit of water with abiding charm. Such are the lakes of Killarney, with their legends woven about a ruined castle and its magic Blarney stone. No wonder lovers of nature have been attracted to such retreats the world over.

Walden Pond in Massachusetts will always be remembered as the spot where Thoreau withdrew from a world which puzzled and annoyed him to live his life of courageous independence. More famous still is the lake region of northern England which nurtured a whole group of gifted writers. Here, over an area of seven hundred square miles in Cumberland, Westmoreland, and Lancashire, mountain, lake, and waterfall are mingled in delightful profusion. True, the mountains seem unimpressive against the stupendous ramparts of the Himalayas or even the Alps, for their loftiest peak, Scafell Pike, is only 3210 feet high. Nor are the lakes themselves of imposing dimensions, for the largest, Windermere, is little more than ten miles long, nowhere a mile in width, with an area of but 5.69 square miles. The lakes of Scotland, Norway, and Switzerland are far more profound than Wast Water's deepest sounding, 258 feet. But it was to this peaceful region, far removed from the seething turmoil of London or the tense activity of Liverpool's docks, that men of letters have sojourned as to a Mecca. Here Sir Walter Scott and Alfred Tennyson loved to come. De Quincey dreamed away nineteen years at Grasmere. John Ruskin preferred Brantwood on Coniston as the one locality in which to pass his declining days. Here Southey, laureate of England, and that inspired genius Coleridge made their homes.

But the poet above all others whose writings overflow with the wisdom of nature, there revealed to his discerning eye, was

William Wordsworth. Sixty years of his fruitful life were passed at Hawkshead, Grasmere, and Rydal Mount, while in the little churchyard at Grasmere the great poet and his devoted wife lie asleep, amid the scenes they loved so well.

LAKES vs. CLIMATE

Lakes have a considerable influence upon our global climate. In some cases their check upon extremes of temperature is almost oceanic. That huge reservoir, Lake Baikal, tempers the rigors of the Siberian winter over an extensive area of Central Asia; vineyards and peach orchards flourish in the favorable environment of Lake Erie; while the January mercury plunges to lower levels in the Dakotas than on the shores of Great Slave Lake, a thousand miles nearer the Pole. Lakes also modify excessive summer heats as countless city dwellers realize when they hasten to spend the week end at some cool waterside. Ladoga, Europe's biggest lake, treats the city of Leningrad to a touch of autumn temperatures in midsummer, while the searing heat of South Australia would be less fearsome were the dry beds of Eyre and Frome and Torrens filled once more with water.

But lakes are less important as regulators of temperatures than as gigantic humidors. They endow the atmosphere with a saving grace of moisture. While water vapor is nearly always present in the air, it touches the vanishing point over such sun-baked regions as Death Valley. Conditions were better, we may be sure, when a deep lake filled the bed of Furnace Creek and washed the foothills of the Funeral Mountains. There are no lakes in the Sahara.

Lakes are also stabilizers of an all-important water supply. Natural catch basins, they conserve the prodigality of floods against the meagerness of droughts. The wadis of Arabia present no happy medium between dust and deluge. For a brief time they brim with swollen torrents, only to become once more bone-dry and blistering ravines. There are no lakes in Arabia.

Lakes are often the final destination of upland waters. To take issue with a biblical statement, not "all the rivers run into the sea," for perhaps a fourth of the land surface of the globe drains into interior basins where lakes, salt or fresh, become the great depositories of surplus moisture. The Volga, largest of European rivers, empties into the isolated Caspian, as do the lesser Ural and the Terek; the Oxus and the Jaxartes flow into the Aral Sea; the impetuous Helmand bursts from the highlands of Afghanistan to deluge the Seistan lakes with melted snows; while the Tarim wanders for nearly a thousand miles between lofty mountains to lose itself at last in the saline barrens of Lop Nor. Even the Murray-Darling, Australia's biggest river, forces only an intermittent exit to the sea. Two thirds of all upland rainfall has its origin in lakes, rivers, growing vegetation, and the exposed soil in an endless cycle of rising mists, condensing clouds, and falling showers.

In the efflorescence of life upon this planet, the circulation of moisture is vital. That celestial motor, the sun, generates the power which raises the waters by evaporation and distributes them through the endless currents of the winds. These, however, are far from impartial in their favors, for they not only give but take away, sometimes robbing the impoverished earth of its moisture just as swarms of locusts strip the foliage from growing vegetation. The insatiable thirst of the heated and expanding air is almost unbelievable. At zero temperatures (Fahrenheit) a cubic foot of air can support less than half a grain of water; at 50 degrees it can support four grains; at 100 degrees, nearly twenty. Hence the absorbent power of the atmosphere may be forty times greater in summer than in winter.

The effect of such accelerated evaporation is astonishing. Over Arabia this has been estimated at 160 inches of water annually. In the desert fringe of South Africa, although the yearly rainfall may be 30 inches, the rate of evaporation is 90. Here ocean currents play the villain's role. Clouds engendered by the cool Benguella Current to drift over the heated interior not only yield no moisture but display an insatiable appetite for more. The chill Humboldt Current off Peru gives that country its famous rainless coast. Foureau, on the edge of the Sahara, observed a thundershower discharging into the upper air, but not a drop of water reached the ground. Heated intervening layers drank it greedily. Under such conditions the winds may wipe away all moisture from the earth as though with a gigantic sponge.

There are two kinds of global water supply, surface and subterranean, both linked in an indissoluble partnership. What impairs one impairs the other; and while we are more concerned with visible ravages, what goes on beneath the surface may prove quite as disastrous.

The average rainfall over the United States is 30 inches annually, enough to fill Lake Michigan's basin to overflowing. Roughly half of this vast downpour is sucked up again in evaporation by the atmosphere; roughly one third runs off in rivers and streams; the remaining one sixth is absorbed by growing vegetation or sinks into the earth.

This "ground water" at first subsides, then spreads out beneath the surface. The rate of dispersal varies with the underlying soil or rock. In Western irrigation ditches water seeps outward at a rate varying from one foot in twenty-four hours to fifty, depending upon the relative coarseness of the soil. In the sandstone strata underlying much of Illinois and Wisconsin that rate is about half a mile a year.

The upper surface of this ocean underground is the so-called water table. Its elevation varies but is higher in lofty than in low-lying terrain. Sometimes it is so near the surface that it gushes forth in springs. Where natural depressions penetrate that table, it appears in innumerable ponds and lakes. This mine of waters, however, is often lowered by those human activities which are forever upsetting the balance of nature. What goes on upon the surface is soon made evident underground. Forests are the great conservers of moisture and forested lakes almost perfect reservoirs. Cut off those forests, however, and the lakes they once enclosed begin to wither. In Central Africa, where the natives have burned over great areas to provide farm and grazing land, the effect upon even the largest lakes is becoming apparent. For a healthy plant is like a fountain spraying the atmosphere with moisture. It takes up water quickly, only to give it off again in that complicated function called transpiration. In the production of one bushel of corn it has been estimated that corn plants diffuse into the air two and a half tons of water.

Diminishing surface waters are soon reflected in the level of the submerged water table. A stirring of the soil with a consequent evaporation may prove disastrous. In the wheat belt of the Dakotas the water plane has fallen so that many lakes have dwindled or disappeared. Even overgrazing, which destroys the grass roots, exposes the earth to such wind erosion as produced the forlorn Dust Bowl of the West.

In the eastern United States it has been estimated that the water table has been lowered from ten to forty feet by cutting down forests and intensive cultivation of the soil. As a result three quarters of the springs and shallow wells have gone dry. In some regions of the earth the water table has fallen so low that even artesian wells fail to reach it.

Upon the spread of civilization and its disastrous influence upon the available water supply, Prince Kropotkin wrote an arresting treatise. His contention—"Is the earth drying up?"— was proved to his satisfaction by the barrens of Central Asia.

He also outlined a happier era called "the former lake period" when the landscape was sprinkled with lakes since become salt marshes or entirely disappeared.

Hand in hand with that unsolved problem, is the earth becoming warmer? goes the less inviting prospect, is it also becoming drier? On the former question two schools of thought argue from what are perhaps insufficient data, but there seems no doubt about the latter. Lakes are disappearing at an accelerating pace, which should give us pause. Of the four thousand which dotted the state of Connecticut at the end of the Ice Age, at least twenty-five hundred have disappeared. It has been estimated that half the lakes in Minnesota will dry up within fifty years. Lakes are not only the visible bastions of defense against a spreading desiccation, but their decline warns us of what is going on beneath the surface in a subsiding water table. The full moon upon a cloudless night discloses no lakes upon its dreary surface. And there is no life either.

XI

Man Intrudes Upon the Stage

SHALL WE HAVE A WATER FAMINE?

Authorities have predicted that within the foreseeable future it may become necessary to ration water in the United States. Such rationing is already commonplace over vast areas of the earth.

In deserts nothing is so precious as that bounty of the clouds, so little regarded elsewhere. Deserts do not cure themselves, but spread like a sort of global eczema. As lakes dwindle and disappear, the atmospheric thirst grows more insatiable. A spreading aridity blights the semifertile fringes of deserts, involving even greater areas. With declining moisture the rate of evaporation climbs. Let a desert once become established and nature not only abandons it but condemns increasing terrain to a similar fate. For lack of water millions of square miles of fertile soil are unfit for human habitation. A single rain clothes the Peruvian desert with verdure, to wither in succeeding droughts. Chad, that former colossus among lakes, has become little better than a marsh before the enveloping Sahara. Only saltbush and similar starveling vegetation survives about the margins of those vast dead lakes which once moistened the now parching atmosphere of South Australia.

Thirst impels even savage animals to call a truce about the communal water hole. Nations might well follow their example by laying aside implements of war and bloodshed to concentrate on preserving the precious water so vital to all.

Water to drink is but a fraction of the needs of our complex civilization. A daily intake of half a gallon may suffice for the individual, but the per capita requirements for city dwellers in the United States has been estimated at 127 gallons. This varied from 48 gallons in Fall River, Massachusetts, to 430 in Tacoma, Washington. No doubt much was wasted, but vast amounts are needed for sewage disposal and manufacturing enterprises.

Few natural resources have been more shamefully mismanaged than our global water supply. The reckless destruction of forests, coupled with unwise agricultural methods, has encouraged a devastating soil erosion. Rains that run off abruptly mar the landscape with unsightly gullies. A wealth of fertility accumulated through slow millenniums has been squandered in a few seasons. And as surface supplies are dissipated, the submerged water table recedes ever deeper into the earth.

Second only to sheer waste is water pollution. Impure drinking water has become a world menace. In many parts of the Old World untreated surface waters, even from springs, are a positive peril to life. Nor is the New World less culpable. The sewage from more than twelve million persons pours into the Great Lakes, which still remain vast reservoirs of drinking water. Such dumping of urban filth is duplicated in lesser lakes. Even more of a threat is water contamination by chemicals and other waste products of manufacturing. Many streams and some considerable rivers are so befouled that they poison the fish.

The spectacle is all the more tragic because there is water in plenty, if it could be wisely conserved and equitably distributed. Some areas have a superabundance. Canada is an apt illustration, with its profusion of lakes, swollen streams, and boggy muskegs. Enough fresh water pours out of the Amazon River to supply the world!

PROBLEMS OF DISTRIBUTION

Irrigation projects were common in Egypt and Babylonia before the dawn of history. The surplus waters of the Nile and the Euphrates were close at hand and easily distributed. The Nile Valley remains one of the garden spots of the world, but when the ferocious Mongols broke up the canals of Babylonia, they condemned an almost equal fertility to mingled swamp and dust.

About one half the irrigated land now under cultivation is in India, where it sustains the swarming population of that too crowded peninsula.

In the United States the Mormon settlement which developed the arid valley about Great Salt Lake proved what intelligent irrigation could accomplish. The area around Phoenix, Arizona, and the Imperial Valley in California are more recent and even more impressive examples. Probably one third of earth's surface is too dry for agriculture without some irrigation. And such projects, as we shall presently observe, have given an impetus to the preservation of existing lakes and the creation of new ones which augurs well for the future. Enthusiastic devotees have estimated that irrigation would double the value of every important farm crop in the United States, where 45,000,000 acres or about the area of the state of Missouri, are available. Imaginative astronomers have even thought that they detected irrigation canals upon the planet Mars! But such planned distribution, like a two-edged sword, may harm as well as help, since it involves man's intrusion into the complicated economy of nature.

By diverting water from inflowing streams, the levels of many lakes are lowered and their existence threatened. Even the Aral Sea, one of the most considerable bodies of inland water in the world, has suffered from the canals which sap the current of the Oxus River.

In the central valley of California irrigation projects have so lowered the underlying water table that areas where wells once flooded at depths of ten to twenty feet are now dry at two hundred and fifty, and thousands of acres of cultivable land have been abandoned. Perhaps 10 per cent of irrigation is supplied from artesian wells. But such waters are often hard and their mineral content ultimately impairs fertility. In time they may make the soil alkaline and leave it "waterlogged." Paramount considerations are *immediate need* and *justifiable cost*. Reclamation projects, unless economically productive and required by expanding populations, are of doubtful benefit.

While irrigation may disturb prevalent water levels, drainage is sure to do so. Drainage ditches convert shallow lakes into swamps, swamps into drying mud. Where lakes are too numerous such operations may be desirable. Nature adopted them upon a gigantic scale when she transformed so much of ancient Lake Agassiz into the silted wheat fields of the Northwest. Some lesser lakes might be spared to equally good purpose, but more rather than fewer lakes is the prevalent need.

Swamps, although they also conserve surplus water and provide climatic humidors, are not so readily defended. As they tend to become breeding places for malaria, mosquito-control projects which drain wide areas will doubtless multiply to the public benefit. In the days of King Alfred, much of England was bog or reedy fen. The drying-out process, when civilization spread, was a decided improvement. It has been estimated that in the eighth century one twentieth of all the tillable land in Europe was too water-soaked for profitable use. Here the problem was too much rather than too little water.

In the United States drainable swamplands total 79,000,000 acres, an area twice that of all New England. Most of this soggy terrain lies in those Southern states which border the Gulf of Mexico—Arkansas, Louisiana, Mississippi, and particularly Florida, where interminable swamps embrace Okeechobee, a shallow lake of nearly 1200 square miles. Yet much acreage here reclaimed at public expense has remained unutilized and not a little is tax-delinquent. Drainage operations beyond immediate needs are always of problematical value.

To be sure, there must be a happy medium between the saturation of the Canadian Shield or the Florida Everglades on the one hand and the dry wastes of the Kalahari and the Gobi deserts on the other. And so mankind has tried irrigation where there was too little water, and drainage where there was too much. Unfortunately, in upsetting the established balance of nature, he has sometimes made a bad matter worse. Attempts to remodel the globe can be detrimental rather than beneficial, and should be undertaken only with a farsighted appraisal of consequences. For the tempo of aeons cannot be changed too abruptly without producing unlooked-for and often unwanted results.

UNDEVELOPED LAKE BEDS

Perhaps the most singular features of upland topography are yawning depressions which lie below the level of the sea. These form ideal lake beds, yet some of them are only dismal marshes and others among the driest spots on earth.

Usually they mark the beds of ancient lakes or seas. Dreary and forsaken, they seem to mourn their lost waters while waiting for the engineering enterprise of the future to restore them.

The Caspian, though hugest of all lakes, occupies only a portion of its much vaster basin. Its surface is now more than 86 feet below sea level, and the persistent decline, recognized for centuries, has become strangly accelerated during the past decade, to the concern of Russian scientists.

Most famous of such depressions in the United States is Death Valley. Lying in Inyo County, California, not far from the Nevada line, it is 150 miles in length with a width varying from 10 to 35. Its sinister name was bestowed by a survivor of the little party of thirty persons, typical forty-niners, who tried to force their way across its burning sands in the days of the California gold rush. Eighteen of the party perished of thirst.

This evil sink lies 276 feet below sea level, exposing the bed of fossil Lake Manly, absorbed by a climate whose consuming thirst is little short of terrific. In August the atmosphere shows but five tenths of one per cent water vapor, and sometimes none at all. The annual rainfall at Greenland Ranch is only 1.4 inches. In 1817 the temperature rose to 100 or above throughout 113 consecutive days. For 43 consecutive days it topped 120 degrees. On July 10, 1913, it hit 134. Since that time a high of 137 has been reported.

Death Valley seems endowed with a poisonous loveliness. Around its edges springs and even pools of water seep out from the surrounding mountains. These mountains are daubed with glaring color—red, yellow, green, brown, and black. Borax fields, once extensively worked, have been abandoned for more productive deposits elsewhere.

The lifeless depression of Eyre Valley in South Australia lies 39 feet below sea level. If this dreary waste of dust, salt, and gypsum once more became a sheet of water, it would impart a welcome moisture to one of the most arid regions on earth.

During the recent World War the high tide of German

invasion in North Africa paused at the Alamein Line. This fortified barricade stretched from the Mediterranean to a forlorn region known as the Qattara Depression which could not be outflanked because it bordered the Sahara. Here the British managed to stave off a threatened conquest of Egypt and a collapse of the entire Near Eastern defense.

This depression covers many thousand square miles, its deepest portions 440 feet below sea level. Some moisture seeps upward from the underlying water table, creating a mixture of thin sheets of water, boggy marsh, and drifting dune. To add to the hazards of the impassable terrain, the summer heat is little less than appalling. This vast excavation in the earth surface is supposedly due to wind erosion.

The Qattara Sink, however, is not the only raw spot on the northern edge of Africa, seared by the sun and fretted by the winds. More famous is the Faiyum Depression in Egypt, scene of one of the great engineering enterprises of ancient times. But that attempt to make something worth while out of a waste area deserves separate mention, as it forecasts a far-reaching program of the immediate future.

MYSTERIOUS MOERIS

The ancient Sumerians, while irrigating the fertile Babylonian valley, excavated pools, just as the cisterns of Hindustan were sometimes enlarged to reservoirs. But the first authentic attempt to create a new lake occurred in Egypt. Here, in the desert area, to the west of the Nile, lay a body of water which has been invested with legend for more than two thousand years. Herodotus has left us a graphic picture. After describing that eccentric structure known as the Labyrinth, he adds, "More marvelous is the Lake Moeris by which it stands. This has a circuit of 3600 furlongs, which is as much as the whole seaboard of Egypt. Its length is from north to south; the deepest part has a depth of 50 fathoms. That it has been dug out and made by man's hands the lake shows by itself." As evidence he noted two pyramids half submerged, crowned by colossal figures. He also explained how the lake was filled from the annual inundation, "by canal from the Nile it flows out into the lake and six months back into the river." This alternate ebb and flow was regulated by locks and floodgates. Evidently the same masterful engineers who designed the Pyramids and the great Temple of Karnak solved the basic problem of artificial lake construction and the utilization of floodtime waters which is now being copied in various reclamation projects throughout the world.

When Alexander the Great's unwieldy empire collapsed, the Ptolemys who inherited Egypt introduced Grecian enterprise. According to tradition, Ptolemy II instructed his engineers to drain off much of Lake Moeris to provide fertile farmland. Like some misguided projects of the present day, this was a mistake. The shrunken lake degenerated into a brackish pool, which now occupies the lowest part of the original Great Depression: an ill-favored body of water known as Birket Qarun with an area of 669 square miles.

Modern geologists, however, do not accept Herodotus's opinion that Moeris was entirely "man-made." It lay in the midst of the Faiyum Depression, an extensive region of 12,000 square miles. Like the deeper Qattara Depression, its origin is ascribed, at least in part, to wind erosion.

Moeris was so near the Nile that it could readily be flooded by that great river. A similar project has converted a desert in southern California into a garden spot. Here the famous Salton Sink, a salt marsh 30 miles long by 12 broad, occupied the lowest part of the Imperial Valley 280 feet below sea level, deeper even than Death Valley. Water from the Colorado

River has been diverted, forming a brackish lake of 287 square miles whose surface has been stabilized at a level still 245 feet below that of the Gulf of California. Irrigation ditches crisscross what is now a fertile area.

In those arid regions which border the great Kalahari Desert in South Africa, Professor E. H. Schwartz and others have advocated diverting several rivers into the Makarikari Playa to restore the former vast lake. This might arrest the encroachments of the desert and provide extensive pastoral and agriculture lands now all but worthless. Opposing engineers, however, have cited the inadequacy of available river volumes against the frightful rate of evaporation.

Where fresh water is unavailable, it has even been proposed to fill vacant depressions with water from the sea. Four thousand square miles of the Qattara Depression lie at least 160 feet below sea level. From the Mediterranean, only forty miles away, a gigantic tunnel has been suggested through intervening terrain too lofty for a canal. A daily intake of 40,000,000 tons would be required to offset the terrific evaporation, but the supply is, of course, inexhaustible. So much moisture added to the bone-dry atmosphere of the Sahara could not fail to be salutary. Besides, the vast intake would generate enormous water power in a region where neither coal, petroleum, nor water power now exist. To harness the sea to such productive effort and at the same time restore a lost fertility to regions once the granaries of Rome is an intriguing prospect.

A similar plan has been outlined in South Australia in the vast plains surrounding empty Eyre. True, the depression is much less, the engineering problems more formidable. But even sea water would be welcome in that region of flaming heats and powdery desiccation.

NEW RESERVOIRS OF WEALTH

Russian savants, alarmed because the surface of the Caspian has subsided six feet or more during the past decade, advocate restoring former levels by diverting the Oxus River from its present outlet to the Aral Sea. For the wheat fields of southern Russia and the Ukraine are threatened with progressive desiccation by the parching winds of Asia. If this hugest of all lakes is menaced by a global drying up, we may well feel concerned over the fate of many lesser ones.

Diverting rivers may prove the answer in some cases. A few small lakes within the city limits of Minneapolis have even tapped the subterranean water table with artesian wells. Far more feasible, however, is the creation of new lakes, by the construction of dams at strategic points in river valleys.

An early example is the great Assouan Dam across the Nile in the region of the cataracts. Although sentimental dreamers like Pierre Loti mourned the drowning of ancient Egyptian temples in the "golden silence," this vast engineering triumph impounds 326,000 acre-feet of water, enough to provide irrigation for 80 per cent of Egypt's farmlands.

The first consideration of such projects is to assure some control over the fresh-water supply. Nature is prone to vacillate between the prodigality of flood and the penury of drought. Both are not only a tragic waste, but enormously destructive. The deluge is pictured in the Book of Genesis as the first world calamity, and floods remain one of the most terrifying of visitations. The Johnstown Flood which sent a pent-up river careering through a populous Pennsylvania valley was a national horror. But it would have been only a minor incident elsewhere. When the Yellow River burst its banks to gouge out a new channel to the sea, ten million hapless Chinese perished!

Floods are a kind of delirium of the elements; drought a wasting sickness. Flood wreckage may be restored in a year or two; prolonged droughts may induce anemia of soil and climate that persists for decades. The great drought of 1934 depressed the underlying water table as much as thirty feet over wide areas. The best remedy for both flood and drought is the creation of new lakes by the damming of rivers.

Simplest of such projects are those designed to supply water to metropolitan areas. Some of these man-made reservoirs, like those which serve Boston and New York, are lakes of considerable size and scenic charm.

Among projects designed primarily to control floods, that of the Tennessee Valley is pre-eminent. Warfare against aridity has enlisted many artificial lakes in California, the far Northwest, and the dry Southwest.

Such waterways are also an incentive to commerce. In the pioneer days of the Hudson's Bay Company Canadian lakes and rivers were valued mainly as navigation routes for birch-bark canoes and clumsy York boats. Even now the Great Lakes above all else are waterways for a fabulous commerce. In the Tennessee Valley the elaborate series of lakes also assures passageway for boats of considerable draft, where formerly the channel was a torrent in floodtime, a mere trickle in drought.

Artificial lakes offer a favorable environment for many forms of wild life. Sportsmen welcome the growing numbers of birds and fish. The latter may provide a substantial revenue. In the Norris Reservoir 275,000 pounds of fish were caught during a fifty-nine-day open season. TVA lakes in northern Alabama yielded over 500,000 pounds of marketable fish during the season of 1946, while two similar reservoirs in Tennessee supplied 200,000 pounds.

An important item in lake values is recreation. In Michigan this ranks as the second largest industry. Many a town, built up around Minnesota lakes, supplies rural communities with their principal tax revenue, a situation widely duplicated elsewhere.

On placid Lake Mead, where the Colorado once dashed through cavernous gorges, 250 pleasure craft now sail. To this Alpine water, in its setting of painted mountains, 840,000 tourists flocked in a single year. Across the top of Hoover Dam, which imprisons the river, 108,528 visitors passed in the single month of August 1939.

In Guntersville Lake of the TVA system in Alabama, a 70-mile sail beckons the voyager along shores abloom with rhododendron. Up the vast lake created by the dam at Grand Coulee on the Columbia River, a 360-mile excursion into Canada is now scheduled. Texoma Lake in Texas, with its 120-mile shore line, introduces a welcome bit of ocean into that vast expanse of dusty terrain.

Still more imposing is the development of water power. This "white coal," which established manufacturing interests in northern Italy where other coal was unobtainable, is running to waste the world over. According to the United States Survey, one half of the world's water power lies in the tropics. Africa seems the most liberally endowed of continents for one third the global total originates in its broad rain belt and the neighboring island of Madagascar. The Colorado and Columbia are minor streams compared with the vast Congo, the second river in the world, in its precipitous descent from the interior tablelands to the sea. Only a fraction of the energy of the Nile has yet been utilized. At Victoria Falls the Zambezi makes a sheer drop of 336 feet.

In South America some of world's greatest waterfalls rouse only echoes in the jungle. Iguassú is world-famous, but greater volumes occur elsewhere. Paulo Affonso in Brazil is said to have a minimum flow of 354,000 cubic feet a second against Niagara's maximum of 314,000. Through less spectacular Guayra Gorge, in the same country, rushes an alleged flood-time torrent of 2,660,000!

Half the potential water power of the globe is concentrated in glaciated uplands. The Canadian Shield, a recognized storehouse of mineral wealth, may yet become a beehive of activity when its brimming lakes and swollen rivers are exploited.

Estimates allot to the waters of the United States 100,-000,000 horse power, several times the total developed from all present sources. In bending such elemental forces to his will, man is subduing far mightier genii than any exotic fancies of *The Arabian Nights*.

Across the curtain rising upon the stage of coming events, however, a word of caution should be inscribed. Electricity from water power is seldom cheap. Sources are usually far from populous centers. The cost of transmitting power is many times that of installation. Moreover, such power is often variable. The Tennessee River, for example, with a floodtime flow of nearly 500,000 cubic feet a second, has dwindled to 4000 feet in time of drought. Hence coal-burning equipment is required to guarantee an even supply of electric current. And there are lesser obstacles. Artificial lakes may be short-lived, as they often tend to silt up rapidly. The reservoir above Roosevelt Dam in Arizona lost 6 per cent of its capacity during a period of twenty-four years. In the Imperial Valley in California it has been found necessary to install silt deposit basins and silt scrapers. Legal complications sometimes arise. The laws which govern lakes are not well integrated. In certain states lakes are privately owned; in others the property of the commonwealth. Arizona and Nevada wrangled interminably over the building of Hoover Dam. Even international disputes may occur, like those between Mexico and the United States over control of the Colorado River and the Rio Grande.

But, after all, these are minor incidents in that conquest of nature which has made such gratifying progress through the control of rivers and the creation of lakes.

MODERN MIRACLES

For countless ages the Colorado River ran riot through the tremendous chasm called the Grand Canyon, until engineers dared to place in its path that amazing obstruction known as Hoover Dam. In ancient times this would easily have displaced any one of the seven wonders of the World. Fashioned like a gigantic horseshoe, steel bands reinforce its 3,250,000 cubic yards of concrete. Buttressed on the gigantic flanks of mountains, it rears 726 feet, a dizzier altitude than that of the Washington Monument. And now behind its battlements the chastened river backs up to form Lake Mead, the largest artificial reservoir in the world.

The area of this lake is 157,736 acres or 246 square miles; its content, 31,141,755 acre-feet or over 92 cubic miles. This is more than four fifths the volume of Lake Erie and represents two years' impounded flow of the Colorado River. Near the dam the lake is 584 feet deep.

The Great Pyramid of Egypt is a useless monument to a Pharaoh's vanity; Hoover Dam the source of incalculable public benefits. Surplus waters flow all the way to the great city of Los Angeles through an aqueduct 392 miles long. Huge dynamos whirr endlessly, converting the once wasted energy of the river into productive power. The operation leaves the water unchanged, merely extracting in transit the hidden force imparted by gravity. Such are a few of the more readily assessable values.

Still more gigantic is the Grand Coulee Dam across the

Columbia River. Here enormous lava floods solidified in basaltic rock. During the glacial age a spur of the continental icecap blocked the river channel, raising the waters enormously to send them surging through this weird region. The boisterous river eroded a gorge 50 miles long and 800 feet deep, varying in width from one to five miles. It excavated 40 cubic miles of solid rock, to plunge at last over a cliff more than a mile wide and 450 feet high in what must have been the grandest waterfall on earth. As the glacial ice melted, the river resumed its former bed, leaving this dry escarpment dangling, as it were, 653 feet above. Across the Columbia near this point a prodigious dam has been constructed, 4300 feet long, 50 feet thick at the top and 500 at the base, a cubic content more than four times that of the Great Pyramid.

Against this barrier the river now backs up for 151 miles in a new lake with an area of 81,000 acres or 126 square miles, 350 feet deep at the lower end and impounding 9,517,000 acre-feet of water. Nor is this all. The vacant depression on the cliffs above was too inviting to be ignored. To fill that depression and create another new lake, ten great pumps, fed by the power of the imprisoned river, have been designed to lift 30,-000 tons of water every minute to a height of 280 feet. These pumps, working for two and a half hours out of the twenty-four, could supply all New York City. They replenish and sustain a lake whose waters sluice off in irrigation ditches to enrich a wide territory formerly unproductive. To employ a homely figure, engineering skill compels a great river to lift itself by its bootstraps, and forces water literally to run uphill. This is, indeed, a striking change from Bryant's familiar lines:

> . . . where rolls the Oregon, and hears no sound
> Save his own dashings . . .

The Bureau of Reclamation may well feel proud of these, its chief exhibits, since it was established by Congress in 1902.

In the intervening years it has constructed no fewer than a hundred dams, a hundred new lakes. Three other government agencies now co-operate in similar projects: the War Department through its Corps of Engineers; the Office of Indian Affairs under the Department of the Interior; and, most advertised of all, the Tennessee Valley Authority, better known as TVA. Besides, many dams and lakes are the result of private enterprise.

When the importation of phosphates from Germany was shut off during World War I, the government undertook to harness the Tennessee River in the production of much-needed fertilizers. With the declaration of peace, the costly experiment was abandoned. Then, during the bleak days of depression, when Washington was trying to start the wheels of industry by making work for the unemployed, the project was revived with a threefold purpose: to control floods, provide river navigation, and to create water power.

Through a fog of antagonism and misunderstanding the TVA is now emerging as one of those modern miracles to which mankind may point with satisfaction against such manifest misdeeds as rocket bombs and biological warfare. For no other river in the history of the world has been so thoroughly broken and harnessed to public use.

Across the Tennessee River and its tributaries twenty-six major dams have created twenty-six lakes, with a total storage volume of 22,023,400 acre-feet. These lakes have a combined area of 595,240 acres, a shore line of 10,058 miles. The Fontana Dam is the highest, 480 feet, the Norris Dam perhaps the best known. Two hundred and sixty-five feet high and 1860 feet long, this great structure creates a lake 72 miles long with an area of over 34,000 acres, a storage capacity of 2,567,000 acre-feet.

Still more imposing is the Kentucky Dam across the Tennessee River near its outlet into the Ohio. This is 8412 feet long,

206 feet high, and required 1,325,000 cubic yards of concrete and 4,000,000 cubic yards of earth. The resultant lake has a shore line of 2200 miles, a volume of 6,002,600 acre-feet, and an area of 158,300 acres, slightly more extensive than Lake Mead.

Where a devastating torrent once flayed the soil from impoverished valleys, conservation projects have developed new farms with buildings lighted by electricity. Pages of statistics might present the tons of phosphate produced or the kilowatt hours generated. But a more sweeping appraisal is the higher standard of living made possible in once backward regions where 3,274,000 people dwell and the realization that nature's wasted bounties may be enlisted in the service of mankind.

Still greater triumphs are planned for the future. Such is the Missouri River Project, where the Bureau of Reclamation, joining hands with the United States Corps of Engineers, recommends a colossal strait jacket for the unruly Big Muddy that dwarfs all present undertakings. More than a hundred dams have been blueprinted, impounding lakes with a storage volume in excess of 45,000,000 acre-feet, enough to flood the state of Pennsylvania beneath a foot of water. Geared with this are thirty power plants with an annual output of four billion kilowatt hours of energy.

And now a side glance at a somber picture, the better to envision the constructive possibilities that lie ahead. To wrest from nature the fatal secret of the atomic bomb, this nation squandered two billion dollars. Like a child playing with matches, man burned his fingers on that expensive bit of fire-works. Nor has the deficit been written off in the red ink of blood and conflagration, in smoldering Japanese cities and heaps of mangled corpses, but a staggering unpaid balance remains in the suspicion that still bedevils international affairs.

An awesome responsibility was ours when we let loose that

demoniac terror upon the world, and we can only hope that the wreck of civilization will not be the ultimate penalty. Prometheus was chained to Caucasus when he stole fire from heaven; but this lurid brand must have been snatched from the deepest gulf of Tartarus. And the human race now finds itself chained to another Caucasus of dire forebodings by fetters of fear and hatred and savagery. Against that appalling background we might well contemplate how a more moderate investment of public treasure, requiring less technical skill, would have preserved the wasted energy of a score of rivers to adorn our landscape with a multitude of friendly lakes.